HEINEMANN GUIDED READERS

UPPER LEVEL

JOHN STEINBECK

The Grapes of Wrath

Retold by Margaret Tarner

HEINEMANN

HEINEMANN GUIDED READERS

UPPER LEVEL

Series Editor: John Milne

The Heinemann Guided Readers provide a choice of enjoyable reading material for learners of English. The series is published at five levels — Starter, Beginner, Elementary, Intermediate and Upper. Readers at **Upper Level** are intended as an aid to students which will start them on the road to reading unsimplified books in the whole range of English literature. At the same time, the content and language of the Readers at **Upper Level** is carefully controlled with the following main features:

Information Control

As at other levels in the series, information which is vital to the development of a story is carefully presented in the text and then reinforced through the Points for Understanding section. Some background references may be unfamiliar to students, but these are explained in the text and in notes in the Glossary. Care is taken with pronoun reference.

Structure Control

Students can expect to meet those structures covered in any basic English course. Particularly difficult structures, such as complex nominal groups and embedded clauses, are used sparingly. Clauses and phrases within sentences are carefully balanced and sentence length is limited to a maximum of four clauses in nearly all cases.

Vocabulary Control

At **Upper Level**, there is a basic vocabulary of approximately 2,200 words. At the same time, students are given the opportunity to meet new words, including some simple idiomatic and figurative English usages which are clearly explained in the Glossary.

Glossary

The Glossary at the back of this book on page 134 is divided into 7 sections. A number beside a word in the text, like this [3], refers to a section of the Glossary. The words within each section are listed in alphabetical order. The page number beside a word in the Glossary refers to its first occurrence in the text.

Contents

The People in This Story

Tom
Son of old Tom and Ma Joad. Tom has just come out of prison. He arrives home to find that his family are being forced to leave their farm and move west to find work.

Ma Joad
The strongest person in the family. Ma tries to keep the family together through all their troubles.

Old Tom Joad
Tom's father. Old Tom has lived all his life in Oklahoma. Now he cannot earn enough money on the farm to pay his debts to the bank. He has decided to leave with his family and travel west to California.

Casy
Casy used to preach religion to people in Oklahoma. He joins the Joad family on their journey.

Rosasharn (Rose of Sharon)
Tom's sister. Rosasharn and her husband, Connie, are expecting their first baby.

Al
Old Tom and Ma Joad's second son.

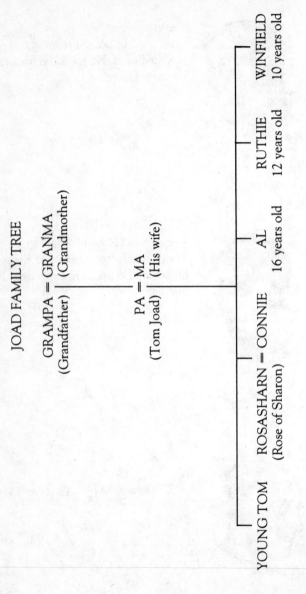

JOAD FAMILY TREE

GRAMPA = GRANMA
(Grandfather) (Grandmother)

PA = MA
(Tom Joad) (His wife)

YOUNG TOM   ROSASHARN = CONNIE   AL   RUTHIE   WINFIELD
             (Rose of Sharon)   16 years old   12 years old   10 years old

Introduction

A Note on the Background

This story is set in North America in the 1930s. For a long time, the small farmers of Oklahoma and other central states of the USA, had grown the same crop – cotton – for year after year and this had made the soil weak. In the 1930s very little rain fell. The poor soil broke up and turned to dust. Then the strong winds blew away the dust and the soil disappeared.

These farmers had to borrow money from the banks. But during the Depression in the late 1920s, trade stopped. Many banks lost their money and had to close. The remaining banks were afraid to lend the money to anyone.

Small farmers like the Joads had no land, no crops and no money. They had all heard of California, with its beautiful weather and large crops of fruit and vegetables. California was a big state and the farmers there needed people to pick their crops. The poor farmers of Oklahoma decided to make the long and difficult journey to the west. They hoped to find work there and one day have land of their own.

But in the rich land of California, the farmers also had problems. There was too much fruit and the farmers could not sell it. They could not pay the people who had come to pick the fruit. The farmers were making no profit and were in debt themselves. They knew that next year their land would belong to the bank. They were afraid that the people from Oklahoma – the Okies – would take their land. The Californians gave the Okies so little money for their work that they and their children starved.

All over the state of California fruit was left to rot. Men burnt the coffee and the corn they had grown. They threw the potatoes into the rivers so that the people could not have them. And fruit was wasted and good food destroyed to keep prices high.

A million hungry people saw good food destroyed. Children starved and the smell of rotting fruit filled the country.

The people wanted to work and they could not. They felt their failure. And in their hungry eyes there was a growing anger.

The Depression had become a time of fear and anger, when Americans began to hate each other. The title of this book, *The Grapes of Wrath*, comes from a song written during the American Civil War (1861–1865), when Americans were fighting Americans. The song tells of the troubles that come to a country when some of its people are not free. Then the 'harvest' of anger or wrath may destroy that country's way of life.

In the souls of the people, the grapes of wrath were ripening. The people were ready now for a terrible harvest – for a time of anger and destruction.

1

The Dust

In Oklahoma, the ploughs cut through the red earth. The rain fell and the corn grew. By the end of May, the sun was strong on the growing corn. The corn grew green and straight. The sun beat down and the earth became dry and pale. In June, the sun was stronger, and the air was thin.

Everywhere, there was dust. Every moving thing raised a cloud of dust. The dust stayed in the air for a long time.

Half-way through June, big thunder clouds moved up from Texas and the Gulf of Mexico. Men looked up into the sky, hoping for rain, but it did not fall. A wind drove the rain clouds to the north. The wind blew harder and the dust rose up from the fields. The wind blew strongly and steadily and the dust was blown away. Then the wind blew on the growing corn.

Day came and a red sun came up, but it gave no light. Men and women had to tie handkerchiefs over their faces when they went out. The night was black, because the dust hid the stars. Houses were shut against the dust, but it still got in and settled on the chairs and tables.

Then the wind passed on and left the land quiet. In the morning, the dust covered the corn, fences, roofs and trees. The people came out of their houses and smelt the hot air. Men stood by their fences and looked at their dying corn. The men were silent and the women came out and stood beside them. They looked at their men's faces. The children stood near and watched too.

After a time, the men's faces became hard and angry. Then the women knew that it was all right. The men would not give up the fight this time. The women went into the houses to work and the children began to play again.

The men sat outside and watched the dust-covered land. They sat still, planning the future, getting ready to fight back.

———

A large red truck slowly came to a stop on the main highway[7], near a narrow dirt[7] road. A young man jumped down and looked up at the driver.

'Thanks for the lift[7],' he said. 'So long[1].' He turned away and walked on to the dirt road.

'Good luck,' called the driver. Then the motor roared and the red truck moved away, raising a cloud of dust.

The young man walking along the dirt road was about thirty years old. His eyes were very dark brown. His lips were firmly closed. His hands were hard, working hands with broad fingers and short thick nails.

The man's shoes were cheap and new. His suit, new too, was of hard grey cloth. He was a tall man and the jacket was too big and the trousers too short. He looked down at his yellow shoes, then bent down and untied the laces. He took off his shoes, then his jacket. He put them under his arm and moved on up the road.

There was a thin wire fence on either side of the road. On the other side of the fence, the corn lay beaten down by heat and wind. The sun was high and the man sweated and walked more slowly. In front of him was a dusty tree which gave a little shade. The young man stood in the shade for a moment and then walked out quickly into the yellow sunlight.

The hot smell of dust filled the air. Then the cornfield ended and there was a field of dark green cotton plants. The bolls of cotton[5] were forming and the dark green leaves were thinly covered with dust. The plants fought against the sun to live. The dirt road stretched out ahead. Dry dust filled the man's eyes and dried them. The road dropped down a little hill and then climbed up again. The man walked on.

Hours later, the sun was losing its heat, but the air was still hot and dry. On the right-hand side of the road, a wire fence ran across the cotton field. The young man walked more quickly. He knew that fence. His father had put up the fence many years before, round the Joads' forty-acre farm.

Tom Joad went on to the top of the next hill. And then he stopped. He looked down at the Joad place[1], his old home. One corner of the small unpainted house had been crushed in. The fences had gone and the cotton grew in the yard and up against the house. The wooden barn[5] lay on its side and dusty cotton grew close against it.

Tom stared for a long time.

No one's living there, he thought. Something's happened, that's sure.

He moved down the hill and looked into the tool-shed, next to the house. There were no tools there. Tom saw an old oilcan, covered with dirt and oil. A pair of torn overalls[7] were hanging from a nail.

Tom moved away to the well. He dropped a piece of earth down the well and listened.

'No water there,' he said aloud. 'Maybe they're all dead. But someone would've[2] told me.'

The front door of the wooden house hung open. There was no furniture in the kitchen, no pots and pans. Tom Joad looked into the bedroom – no bed, no chairs, nothing. In one corner lay a woman's shoe. Tom picked it up and looked at it.

'This was Ma's,' he said. 'It's worn out[7]. Ma liked that shoe. They've moved out. Must have taken everything.'

A thin grey cat came out of the barn. It came silently up to the young man and sat down.

'Why hasn't that cat gone to some neighbours?' Tom asked himself. 'Maybe there aren't any neighbours. Maybe everyone's gone.'

11

A tall thin man was walking through the cotton.

Tom stared across the fields. A tall thin man was walking through the cotton, raising a high cloud of dust. Tom stared at the man's long pale face. Grey stiff hair stood up straight from the high forehead. The man wore overalls and a blue shirt. His canvas shoes were grey with dust.

'Why[4], it's the Reverend[7] Casy! Hey, Casy, how are you?' Tom called out.

'Now aren't you young Tom Joad – old Tom's boy?' Casy called back.

'That's me. Where's my folks[1]?'

'Why, where've you been, Tom? They've moved away to the Rances' place, next farm along. Folks there moved out some weeks ago. When the tractors came. Your folks were going to stay here. Your Grampa stood out here with a rifle. But that rifle couldn't stop a tractor. So they moved on. But how is it you don't know?'

The young man looked down and moved his bare feet in the dust.

'I haven't been home for four years. Didn't you hear? I got sent[3] to jail. I killed a man. He got out a knife and I hit him over the head with a shovel. I got seven years[6], but they've let me out on parole[6]. My folks haven't written for two years. What are they planning to do?'

'I heard they're thinking of going west. Your Pa's going to buy a car. Folks say life is easy out west. You can pick oranges right off the trees.'

Tom looked at the broken house.

'Night after night in jail, I lay on my bunk and thought how it would be when I got home,' he said slowly. 'I knew it wouldn't be the same, but I didn't think it would be like this. Well, I'll go on to the Rances' place in the morning. You coming, Casy? Ma always liked you. Maybe you can come with us, out west. Ma'll like to take a preacher[7] along.'

'I'm not a preacher now,' Casy said, 'but, yeah[1], I'm coming

13

with you. And when you folks start out on the road, I'll be with you.'

'We'll get some sleep now,' Tom said. 'We'll start for the Rances' place tomorrow, early.'

'I ain't[2] sleeping,' said Casy. 'I've got too much to think about. Now I'm not a preacher, I do a lot of thinking.'

He stretched out on his back and looked up at the stars. Tom Joad yawned, covered himself with his jacket and got ready for sleep.

Slowly the life of the night began as small animals crept out of their holes. Mice ran over the hard earth, rabbits moved to anything green and growing. Hunting birds flew silently overhead. The two men slept.

2

The Tractors and the Land

All over Oklahoma the tractors came and the people had to go. The owners of the land came first. They felt the dry earth with their fingers. The tenant farmers[5] watched unhappily from their doorways. Then the owner men drove their cars into the yards and spoke out of their car windows. In the open doors, the women looked out and behind them stood the children. The women and children watched their men talking to the owner men.

Some of the owner men were kind and some of them were hard and afraid. They all said the same thing.

'The Bank[5] owns the land. This land's poor. You know that. And the land's getting poorer. The dust flies away. And cotton robs the soil, takes the life out of it.'

The tenant farmers nodded. They knew all this. Maybe, if they stayed, next year would be a good year.

'We can't be certain. And we've got to pay our debts to the Bank,' said the owner men.

The farmers looked down.

'What do you want us to do? We're half-starved now. The kids are hungry all the time. Our clothes are old and torn.'

'The tenant system[5] won't work any more,' replied the owner men. 'You small farmers must go. One man on a tractor can take the place of twelve or fourteen families. We pay the man a wage, one wage, and take the crop. We have to do it.'

'But you'll kill the land with cotton.'

'We know. We've got to take the cotton before the land dies. Then we'll sell the land.'

'But what'll happen to us? How'll we eat?'

'You've got to get off the land.'

'Grampa took this land from the Indians. I was born here. Our children were born in this house. It's our land. It's ours because we've been born on it, worked it, died on it. That makes us the owners of the land.'

'You're wrong. The Bank owns it. You'll have to go.'

'But if we go, where'll we go? How? We've got no money.'

'We're sorry. But you're on land that isn't yours. Why don't you go west to California? There's work there and it never gets cold. There's peaches and pears in spring and later there's cotton. There's always some kind of crop to pick in California. Why don't you go there?'

The owner men started their cars and moved away.

'Where'll we go?' the women asked.

'We don't know. We don't know.'

The children crowded round the women in the houses.

'What are we going to do, Ma? Where're we going to go?'

15

'We don't know yet. Go out and play. But don't go near your father. He's thinking about things.'

———

The tractors came over the roads and into the fields. They raised the dust in great clouds.

The man sitting on the iron seat of the tractor did not look like a man. He wore gloves, goggles and a rubber mask. He was part of the machine.

The man drove straight over the land, through a dozen farms. He could not see the land properly, he could not smell it and feel it. This man loved the tractor, not the land.

At noon, the tractor driver stopped. Sometimes he stopped near a tenant's house. The hungry children came out to watch him. They stood watching as he unwrapped his sandwiches and ate them.

'What do you get for this kind of work?' the farmer asked.

'Three dollars a day. I've got a wife and kids. We've got to eat. Three dollars a day and it comes every day.'

'But for your three dollars a day, fifteen or twenty families don't eat at all. Nearly a hundred people have no work because of your three dollars a day.'

'I can't worry about that. Times are changing. There's no place for you little farmers any more. You go somewhere else, and try to earn your three dollars a day.'

The tractor driver finished his lunch.

'You'd better leave soon,' said the tractor driver. 'I'm driving right through here later. I've got orders. If you don't move out, maybe I'll push in your home a little. They might pay me extra for that.'

'But I built this house with my own hands. If you knock it down, I'll come after you with a gun.'

16

All of them stared after the tractor.

'That's no good. If you kill me, there'll be another man on the tractor tomorrow.'

The driver started the engine and roared off. He went on and came back. The tractor hit the side of the wall. The house moved sideways. The tractor roared on. The tenant farmer stared after it, his gun in his hand. His wife was beside him. The quiet children stood behind them. And all of them stared after the tractor.

3

The Joads

The two men woke at dawn. Tom and Casy stretched and started on their way at once. They walked in silence and smelt the dust in the air.

A redness came up in the sky and the birds began to sing.

'Look,' said Tom at last, 'there's the Rances' place.' He walked faster.

'I wonder if all the folks are there. I wonder if Ma . . .'

The two men saw the house now, a square little box, unpainted and bare. In the yard, there was a pile of furniture, beds, chairs, tables.

'Great Heavens[4], they're ready to go,' Tom said.

A truck stood in the middle of the yard. It was a strange truck. Once it had been a car. Now, where the back seats had been, wooden planks were nailed down to make the floor of an open truck.

As the men came nearer, the sun rose. Its light fell on the windows of the house and the metal parts of the truck.

'Don't shout out,' Tom said. 'Let's surprise them.'

He walked very fast for a few moments. Then, as he reached the yard, he slowed down. He looked at the front half of the truck that had once been a Hudson Super-Six. Old Tom Joad was working on the back part of the truck.

Tom leant against the side of the truck. His father looked up for a moment and then went on with his work.

'Pa,' said Tom softly.

'What do you want?' said Old Tom, not looking up.

He wore a dirty black hat, a blue shirt, and old jeans. He was a lean strong man with short heavy legs. He had grey hair and his face and eyes were brown.

Old Tom pushed his head forward to see more clearly.

'Tommy,' he said. 'It's Tommy come home.'

A look of fear came into his eyes.

'You haven't broken out of jail? You haven't got to hide?'

'No,' said Tom, 'I'm free. On parole. Got my papers[6] here.'

Old Tom jumped down from the truck.

'Tommy, we're going to California. I was going to write a letter. But now you're back! You can go with us.'

Pa looked over his shoulder.

'Let's surprise your Ma. She's got a bad feeling she's not going to see you again. Come on, let's go in and surprise her.'

Tom said, 'You remember the preacher, Pa. Casy. I met him on the road.'

Pa looked hard at Casy and shook hands.

'You're welcome here, sir.'

'Glad to be here,' said Casy. 'It's good to see a boy come home.'

'Home,' said Old Tom softly. He looked down the road for a moment and then said, 'How'll we tell Ma? Shall I go in and say: "Here's some fellas[1] want breakfast."?'

'Don't scare[7] her,' said Tom.

'Come on,' said Pa. 'I've got to see her face when she sees you. Come on in.'

There was a smell of burning wood from the fire, the smell

19

Tom leant against the side of the truck.

of frying meat, home-made bread and strong coffee. Pa stepped inside and Tom looked at his mother. She looked up but the sun was behind Tom. She nodded to the dark shape in the doorway.

'Come in,' she said. 'Lucky I made plenty of bread this morning.'

Ma was a heavy woman, but not fat. She wore a long loose dress. Her bare feet were broad and strong and she moved quickly as she worked. Her hair was grey and her face was round.

Ma's eyes were not sad, but they had known sadness and pain. Ma was the strong centre of the family and she knew it. She protected her family from all the bad things that were happening to them. If Ma lost her strength, the family would break up.

Tom stepped into the room and walked up to the stove. Ma's eyes opened wide and the fork in her hand dropped to the floor.

'Thank God[4],' she said, 'oh, thank God.' Then suddenly her face was worried.

'Tommy, they ain't after you? You didn't break out?'

'No, Ma, parole.'

She moved towards him, her face full of joy. Her small hand felt his arm and then his face. Tom bit his lip. Ma saw it and she moved away suddenly.

'Well,' she cried, 'we were nearly going without you.'

She picked up the fork and turned back to the stove. She brought out the meat and put it on the plates.

Ma said, 'Pa, run out and tell Grampa and Granma that Tommy's home.'

'Tommy,' Ma said, not looking at Tom, 'Tommy, I've got to ask you. You don't hate everybody? They didn't teach you to be mad with hate in that jail?'

'No . . . o . . .,' said Tom slowly. 'I was mad for a little while, but I kept quiet and everything was OK. I don't hate anyone. But when I saw what they did to our house . . .'

Ma came near to him.

'Tommy, you can't fight the owner men alone. They'll hunt

21

you down. But I've been wondering, dreaming. There's a hundred thousand of us turned out of our homes. If we all fought, the owner men couldn't hunt us down. But folks don't know what to do.'

'Ma,' Tom said, 'I never heard you talk like this before.'

Her face went hard.

'I never had my house pushed over,' she said quietly. 'I never had to sell all my things.'

She turned back to the stove, and put the bread on two tin plates. For a moment Tom watched her, and then he went to the door.

Grampa and Granma were coming across the yard, Pa behind them. Grampa was first, a ragged old man. He was just out of bed and was trying to do up his trouser buttons as he walked. Behind him came Granma.

'Look at him,' cried Grampa. 'He's been in jail for killing a man. But Tom's all right. He did what I'd have done. Where's breakfast?'

Before the others could sit down, Grampa had taken his plate and his mouth was full of bread and gravy. Granma looked proudly up at Tom.

Ma waved the flies away from the bowl of gravy.

'We ain't got enough chairs to sit on. Just take a plate and eat where you can – out in the yard, or somewhere.'

'Come on in, Casy,' called Tom. 'Come in and eat.'

They all started eating and there was no more talk until the food and coffee had gone. When Tom and Pa had finished, they put down their plates and walked over to the truck.

Tom opened the hood[7] and looked at the big engine. Pa came up beside him.

'Your brother, Al, looked at the engine before we bought her. He says she's all right.'

'What does he know about cars? He's just a kid[1],' said Tom.

'He worked for a company. Drove a truck last year. Knows all about engines, Al does.'

'Where's he now?' Tom asked. 'And where's Rosasharn?'

'Al's gone into town to sell some stuff[7]. He took Ruthie and Winfield with him. And your sister's with Connie's folks. But you didn't even know she's married! Connie's a nice young fella. Rosasharn is having her baby in about four months now. She looks fine.'

'She was just a young kid,' Tom said. 'A lot happens when you're away four years. When are you thinking of going out west, Pa?'

'Maybe we can start tomorrow or the day after. A fella told me it's nearly two thousand miles to California. The quicker we get started, the quicker we get there. We're spending money all the time.'

'How much money have you got?' Tom asked. 'I've only got two dollars.'

'Well,' said Pa, 'we sold stuff and we worked in the cotton fields. We got two hundred dollars. We had to give seventy-five for this old car. We've got this stuff in the yard to sell. We'll have about one hundred and fifty dollars when we start.'

The sun was overhead now and the truck's shadow was black on the ground. The truck smelled of hot oil and paint. Pa pulled his hat further down over his eyes.

'Let's get the stuff loaded, Pa,' said Tom. 'Then I can take it into town and pick up Al and the little fellas. I learnt to drive a truck in jail.'

'Good,' said Pa, 'we'll get started. We've got to get out soon.'

4

Ready to Go

In the late afternoon, Tom drove the truck back into the yard. Al was sitting in front with Tom and the others were standing in the back of the truck. Twelve-year-old Ruthie and ten-year-old Winfield – the little fellas were tired but excited. Rose of Sharon was leaning carefully against her husband, Connie. The girl was thinking about her baby and there was a smile on her face.

The men in the truck were angry and sad. They had sold everything they had taken with them for only eighteen dollars. The men knew that their things had been worth much more. But they needed the money quickly.

The engine of the truck was noisy. As Tom stopped the truck, the brakes squealed.

The little fellas jumped down from the truck. They stood looking at Tom, their big brother who had killed a man. Connie helped Rosasharn to the ground. She smiled and walked towards the house, to Ma.

Then, slowly and quietly, the family came together by the truck. This was the most important place now, the place where the family met. The house was dead and the fields were dead, but this old truck was the living centre of the family's life. Pa walked round the truck and squatted down. He picked up a stick and began to draw circles in the dust.

Grampa came out of the house and sat down carefully on the side of the truck. Tom, Al and Connie sat in line with Pa, making a half-circle.

The women took their places, standing behind the men. The children moved their feet in the dust, but made no sound. Casy, the preacher, stayed out of sight, behind the house. He was not one of the family, and this was a family meeting.

Pa spoke softly to the whole group: 'Hundred and fifty-four dollars. That's all we've got. And Al says we need new tyres.'

Al spoke slowly and carefully. He had not spoken at a family meeting before.

'The truck's old and she doesn't look right. But I had a good look at everything before we bought her. She's a popular car. We can always get spare parts[7] cheap. Tyres will be easy to get too.'

Tom said, 'I learnt something about cars in jail. Al's done right[3]. I couldn't have done better myself. Now I've got something to tell you all. Casy – he's the preacher – wants to go west with us. He's a nice fella.'

Pa said, 'I wonder if all of us can ride in the truck, and the preacher too. And can we feed another mouth? Can we, Ma?'

'It ain't "can we?", but "will we?",' Ma said clearly. 'I say we will. The Joad family doesn't refuse food or a ride to anybody that asks.'

Tom stood up and called, 'Casy, oh Casy!'

Casy came quickly round the side of the house and squatted down with the others. He had been accepted as one of the family.

Pa said, 'We've got to work out when to start. The quicker the better now. They say it's two thousand miles. That's a hell of a long way.'

'What are we waiting for, then?' said Al. 'There's nothing more we can do here. Why don't we go? We can sleep on the way.'

Pa stood up.

'We're going now,' he said. 'Let's get the stuff together. It'll take a few hours to load the truck. Come on, you fellas.'

It was dark now. Circles of light from the lanterns began to move about the yard. The men brought together all the things they were taking and put them by the truck.

Rose of Sharon brought out the family's clothes. Tom went to the tool shed and brought out the few tools that were left. And now Rose of Sharon brought out the mattresses and ragged blankets.

Tom came into the kitchen with his lantern.

'Smell that meat!' he said.

Ma looked up at Tom and smiled at him.

'Must have something to eat when we're travelling.'

Tom said, 'Ma, what stuff's to go from here?'

Ma looked quickly about the kitchen.

'The bucket,' she said. 'All the stuff we eat with. All the big pots and pans. You take that stuff. I'll take the other things after I've finished cooking.' Ma picked up a lantern and walked heavily into the bedroom.

The preacher said, 'She looks tired. Maybe she's sick.'

Ma heard his words. Slowly, the lines went from her face. Her eyes sharpened and her shoulders straightened.

She looked around the room and put the lantern on the floor. She sat down beside a small cardboard box, the only thing left in the room. Inside the box were letters, photographs, newspaper cuttings, a pair of earrings and a little gold ring.

Ma put the earrings and the gold ring into an envelope which she put into her pocket. She looked at the papers and the photographs for a few minutes. Then she put them back and closed the box carefully.

She went into the kitchen again and laid the box on the fire. The flames flared up for a few moments and the box was gone.

———

Out in the dark yard, Pa and Al loaded the truck. They made the load as flat as possible. On top of everything they laid the mattresses. At last they spread the big waterproof cover over the load and tied it down to the truck.

'Now, if it rains,' Al said, 'we'll tie the cover to the bar above. Then the folks can get underneath, out of the wet.'

Al looked at his father.

'You glad to be going, Pa?' Al asked.

'Well, yeah. It's been hard here. It'll be different out there. Plenty of work, little white houses to live in, oranges growing everywhere.'

The first grey light of day came into the sky. The work was done. Food was ready too.

The family stood around the house door, shivering a little and eating quickly.

'Guess[1] we ought to wake up Granma and Grampa,' Al said.

The light was brighter now. Tom walked into the house and came out with Grampa.

'He wasn't sleeping,' Tom said. 'There's something wrong with him.'

'Ain't nothing[3] wrong with me,' Grampa said. 'I just ain't going.'

'Not going?' said Pa. 'Why, we're all packed up. We've got to go. We ain't got no place to stay.'

'Well, you go without me,' said Grampa. 'This country ain't no good, but it's my country. I'll stay here, where I belong.'

Pa said helplessly, 'Now listen to me, Grampa . . .'

Tom touched his father on the shoulder.

'Pa, come into the house. I want to tell you something. You too, Ma.

'You got any whisky, Pa?' Tom asked.

'None.'

Ma said, 'Tom, I got half a bottle of medicine I used to send Winfield to sleep when his earache was bad. Will that do?'

'It might,' said Tom. 'Make a strong cup of black coffee, Ma. Then put in all this medicine.'

Grampa stood in the doorway. 'Where's my breakfast?' he said.

He went into the house, drank the coffee and began to eat. Very soon, he put his arms on the table. Then his head rolled and fell onto his arms. The old man was fast asleep.

Now they were ready. Granma was dressed and ready to go. The family stood looking at the land in the pale morning light.

'Come on,' said Tom. 'Let's get Grampa on the truck.'

They picked him up. When they came to the truck, Tom and Al climbed on. They lifted the old man up gently and laid him on top of the load.

Pa said, 'Ma, you and Granma sit in front with Al for a while. We'll change around later.'

They got into the cabin and the others climbed up on top of the load: Connie and Rose of Sharon, Pa, Ruthie and Winfield, Tom and the preacher.

Al started the engine and the truck crawled across the yard. It crawled up a little hill and the red dust rose around them.

'Gee⁴, what a load,' said Al.

Ma tried to look back, but the load was in her way. She straightened and looked ahead. Her eyes were very tired.

Cotton fields lined the road. The truck crawled slowly through the dust, towards the highway and the west.

5

The Way West

The overloaded truck crawled slowly to the highway at Sallisaw and turned west. On the concrete road, Al built up speed to thirty-five miles an hour. They passed through town after town. The sun was overhead and had heated the red dust of the fields.

Al had been driving for many hours. He had become part of the engine. He listened for any noise from the truck that might mean trouble. His eyes looked first ahead and then down at the instrument panel.

'She makes a lot of noise,' Al said, 'but I think she's all right.

But I don't know how she'll climb a hill with this load. Are there any hills between here and California, Ma?'

'I heard it's all hills. Mountains too. Big ones,' Ma said. 'We'll never get over them with all this stuff.'

'Ma, are you scared of going to a new place?' Al asked. 'Are you scared it won't be nice like we thought?'

Ma's eyes grew thoughtful and soft.

'I ain't scared so much. In front of us, there's a thousand different lives we might have. But at the moment it's the road and the journey. And it's how soon the family wants to eat. That's all I can think about.'

The sun reached the highest part of the sky. Steam started to come out of the engine as the water boiled with the heat.

They came to a shack beside the road. In front of the shack were two gas⁷ pumps, a water tap and a hose. As Al drove up and stopped by the hose, a fat, angry-looking man came out of the shack.

'You folks plan to buy anything?' he asked. 'You got money?'

'Sure we've got money. We need gas.'

'Well, that's all right, folks,' said the man. 'Help yourself to water. The road's full of people. A man has to be careful. They come in, use water, maybe steal, and don't buy nothing.'

Winfield took the hose. He drank from it and then poured water over his head and face.

'I don't know what's happening,' the fat man went on. 'Fifty or sixty cars going by every day now. Folks all moving west. Got their kids and all their stuff with them. Where're they going? What're they going to do?'

'They're doing the same as us,' said Tom. 'Looking for some place to live. Trying to get work. That's all. Soon, you may be on the road yourself.'

Al had the hood of the truck up now and he was checking the oil. The fat man filled the gas tank. Tom had poured water from the hose into the radiator.

They came to a shack beside the road.

Everyone moved back slowly to the truck.

'Get up there on top, Al. I'll drive her for a bit,' Tom said.

'All right,' said Al. 'But watch the oil. And take her slow, Tom. She's overloaded.'

Tom laughed.

'I'll watch her,' he said. 'You can rest easy.'

Ma sat beside Granma in the front. Tom took his place and started the engine. The sun was going down the sky in front of them. Tom pulled his cap further down over his eyes.

They had reached Oklahoma City – the big city. Tom drove straight on. Ma woke up and looked at the wide streets. And the family, on top of the truck, stared at the big stores, the tall houses and office buildings. The buildings grew smaller. They were on the outskirts of the city again. Tom drove slowly and carefully in the traffic, and then they were on Highway 66 – the great western road – and the sun was going down now.

Highway 66 was the main migrant[7] road. It had become the path of a people in flight. The migrants were flying from the dust and the tractors, from the winds and the floods. They came onto 66 from the dusty side roads. Highway 66 was the mother road now, the road of flight.

'We stay on this road all the way now,' Tom said.

'Maybe we'd better find a place to stop before sunset,' Ma said. 'I've got to cook meat and make some bread. That takes time.'

'Tom,' Ma said, 'you're on parole, aren't you? What happens when you cross a state line[6]? Can they take you back to jail? If you cross the line, you've done a crime[3].'

'Don't you worry,' Tom said. 'I've thought about that. If I get caught for anything – yes, they'll send me back. If I don't do nothing wrong, they won't care.'

They went on through the next small town and out on the other side. Tom pointed ahead.

'There's some folks camping! Looks like a good place.'

He slowed down and stopped beside the road.

An old car was pulled off the highway. There was a little tent beside it. Smoke came out of a stove-pipe fixed through the side of the tent. The hood of the car was up, and a middle-aged man stood looking down at the engine. He looked up at the Joad truck and his eyes were worried and angry.

Tom leaned out of the window of the truck.

'Any law against stopping here for the night? You've got a right to say if you want neighbours or not.'

The man smiled.

'Why, sure, come off the road. Proud[1] to have you. Sairy,' he called. 'Here's some folks. Come out and meet them.'

A woman came slowly out of the tent. Her skin was dry and her eyes were dark with pain. She was small and thin. But when she spoke, she had a beautiful voice.

'You're welcome,' she said. 'You're all good and welcome[1].'

6

The Death of Grampa

Tom brought the truck into the field and pulled up next to the car. The family got down stiffly from the truck. Ma got to work quickly. She untied the bucket from the back of the truck.

'Now you go and get water,' she said to the children. 'Down there. And if you see any wood for a fire, bring that as well.' The children walked away.

'You're from Kansas,' said Al, looking at the other car. 'I knew you weren't Oklahoma folks. You talk different.'

'Everybody says words different,' said Sairy. 'But we're all the same folks. Our name's Wilson.'

Without warning, Grampa suddenly began to cry. Ma rushed over and put her arms round him.

'Put him in our tent,' Sairy said. 'He can rest for a little on our mattress.'

Ma helped Grampa into the tent. Then she came out and looked at Casy.

'Grampa's sick,' she said. 'Come and take a look at him.'

Grampa lay on his back. His eyes were open, staring upward, and his face was red. He was breathing heavily.

Casy put his hand on Grampa's forehead. As he was looking at the red, twitching face, Ma came in.

'What's wrong?' she said.

'I think he's going to have a stroke[7].'

'I want to see him,' called Granma from outside the tent. 'He ain't ill, he's sulking[7].'

Casy went outside.

'He ain't sulking, Granma, he's sick. Sick real bad[1].'

'Well, then,' said Granma, 'why aren't you praying? You're a preacher.'

Grampa began to struggle. Then his body made one sudden movement and he lay still.

'Our Father, who art in Heaven,' Casy began.

A long sigh came from the old man's open mouth.

'Thy kingdom come . . . Thy will be done on earth . . .'

'Amen!' cried Granma.

The breathing stopped.

'Amen!' said Casy, kneeling by the mattress.

Ma took Granma outside. The family looked at her. Granma sat proudly while the family gathered round. Then suddenly she lay down and covered her face with her arm.

'We're thankful to you folks. He died in your tent,' Pa said.

'We're proud to help,' said Wilson.

Al said, 'Me and Tom'll fix your car.'

Pa said, 'We've got to think what to do with the body. We've only got one hundred and fifty dollars. If we report the death, they'll take forty dollars to bury Grampa.'

33

'What'll we do?' asked Al.

Pa said softly, 'We'll bury Grampa here ourselves. We'll put some writing in a bottle and bury it with him. Something to say who he was, and why he's buried here.'

The men got out the tools for digging. Pa marked out the ground. Ma washed the body and Tom wrote carefully on a piece of paper.

When everything was ready, the two families stood round the grave. Casy said a short prayer.

'Amen,' repeated everyone.

The women moved back to the fire to prepare the supper. The men hurriedly filled in the hole.

Rose of Sharon knelt near the fire and looked at her mother.

'Ma, I'm scared. Will it hurt the baby?'

'Scared?' said Ma. 'Why, you can't get through nine months without sorrow. You forget about yourself and that baby for a while.'

When the meat and potatoes were cooked, the families sat on the ground and ate. They were quiet, staring into the fire.

Ma asked the Wilsons, 'How long have you folks been on the road?'

'We ain't been lucky,' Wilson said. 'We've been on the road three weeks. The car won't run. Starts and stops. It's getting worse all the time.'

'I reckon[1] I can help you,' Al said.

'He's good with a car,' said Pa.

'Well, I sure thank you. It's a lot of trouble getting to California, but it'll be worth it. I've seen handbills telling how they need folks to pick fruit. Good wages, too. In a couple of years, a fella could buy land, have a place of his own . . .'

Pa said, 'We've seen those handbills. I've got one right here. "Pea Pickers wanted in California. Good wages all season. 800 Pickers wanted."'

Wilson looked at the bill.

The two families stood round the grave.

'Why, that's the one I've seen. You think . . . maybe they got eight hundred already?'

'But this is just one little part of California,' said Pa. 'It's the second biggest state we've got.'

Tom and Al walked up to the two older men.

'We've been thinking, Pa,' Tom said. 'Our truck's overloaded, but the Wilsons' ain't. Some of our folks could ride with them and we could take some of their stuff. Then both cars could get up the hills. We'd keep together on the road maybe.'

'I've only got thirty dollars left,' said Wilson. 'I don't want to be a trouble.'

'You won't be a trouble,' said Ma. 'And you helped us with Grampa.'

The Wilsons smiled shyly and looked at the ground.

'We'll see you get there,' Ma said to Sairy. 'Now, come on, we've got to get some sleep tonight.'

The fire died down. There were few cars on the highway now, but the transport trucks roared by.

Soon the families were quiet and sleeping. Only Sairy Wilson lay awake, her eyes wide open with pain.

7

Breakdown

And now the Joads and the Wilsons were on the road again, together. The old truck and the car crawled westward. They crossed the state border and left Oklahoma behind. They went on through Texas.

After three days, the highway became their home. They had changed their whole way of living. Slowly, they settled into their new life. They drove along and the land rolled by, mile after mile.

They came to the end of Texas. Then it was New Mexico and the mountains.

The mountains stood in the far distance, up against the sky. The wheels of the cars turned and turned. The engines got overheated and steam rushed out.

Al drove the Wilson's car. Ma sat beside him and Rose of Sharon next to Ma. Ahead, the truck crawled along, always the same distance away. The air was hot and the mountains shook in the heat.

Ma sat with her hands folded in her lap. Rose of Sharon held herself stiffly against the movement of the car, thinking always of her unborn child.

'Ma,' Rose of Sharon said, 'when we get there, me and Connie have got it all planned. Connie's going to get a job in a store, or maybe a factory. And he's going to study at home, maybe radio, so he can have his own store. Nice clean work and a good future. The baby'll have all new stuff when it's born.'

'We don't want you to go away from us,' Ma said.

Al sat stiffly now, holding the wheel very tightly. He had heard a little rattle in the engine. He went faster, and the rattle got louder. Al blew his horn and pulled the car to the side of the road.

Ahead, the truck pulled up too and backed slowly. Tom got out and called, 'What's the matter, Al?'

Al made the engine roar loudly.

'Listen to her.' The rattling noise was louder now.

Al said, 'It's the con-rod, ain't it?'

'Sounds like it,' said Tom.

Wilson asked, 'Is that bad?'

'Yeah,' said Tom.

Al was unhappy. He felt that the trouble was his fault.

'We'll have to get the rod out and get a new part,' said Tom. 'Then we've got to fit it. It'll take all day. And tomorrow's Sunday. We can't get nothing tomorrow. And we ain't got the tools to make it easy.'

Wilson said, 'It's my fault. This old car of mine's given me trouble all the way. Why don't you folks go on? Me and Sairy'll stay here.'

Tom took off his cap and wiped his forehead.

'I've got an idea,' he said. 'The quicker we get to California, the quicker we start making money. Now this car goes twice as fast as the truck. Unload the truck a little and you folks go on. Me and Casy'll stay here and fix the car. Then we'll catch you up.'

Ma said worriedly, 'How are you going to find us?'

'Don't you worry,' said Tom. 'We'll find you. California ain't the whole world.'

Pa said, 'Well, I guess that we'd better get going. We can maybe do a hundred miles before dark.'

Ma stepped in front of him, 'I ain't going,' she said.

Pa was very surprised. 'What do you mean? You've got to look after the family!'

Ma walked to the car, picked up the jack-handle and held it in her hand. Her mouth was set hard.

'The only way to get me to go, is to beat me. And if you do, I'll hit you with this handle. Come on,' said Ma. 'Just try it.'

Pa looked round helplessly.

The whole group watched Pa, waiting for him to lose his temper, to shout and fight it out. But his anger did not rise. His hands hung loosely at his sides. The group knew that Ma had won. And Ma knew it too.

Tom said, 'Ma, what's the matter with you?'

'You haven't thought much. I have,' Ma said. 'What have we got left in the world? Only the family. Money wouldn't do no good with the family broken up. I ain't scared when we're all together. But I'm going to hit out with this handle if my own family breaks up.'

Tom said quietly, 'Ma, we can't camp here. There's no shade, no water.'

'All right,' said Ma. 'We'll move on and stop at the first place

Ma walked to the car, picked up the jack-handle and held it in her hand.

where there's shade and water. Then the truck'll come back and take you into town.'

Tom looked at her helplessly.

'You win, Ma. Put that handle away before you hurt somebody. Al, you drive the folks on and get camped. Maybe we can still get a con-rod tonight, as it's Saturday. Get me the tools and I'll get started.'

Before the truck had moved away, Tom and Casy were working together on the old car.

After a while, Casy spoke to Tom. 'I've been watching the road. There's hundreds of families – all going west. Did you notice that?'

'Yeah,' Tom said, 'there's a whole country moving.'

'Well, perhaps all those folks can't get jobs out there?'

'I'm not looking ahead,' said Tom, 'I can only think about one thing at a time.'

Tom stood up.

'Ain't that Al coming now?'

The truck pulled up beside the car and Al got out.

'We've had trouble,' Al said. 'Granma started shouting and talking to Grampa. She don't make sense no more. But we found a camp. Costs half a dollar a day to stay there. But everyone's too tired and miserable to move on.'

Al took a paper bag from the seat.

'Here's some bread and meat Ma sent and I've got some water here.'

'She don't forget nobody,' said Casy. 'Look, I'll stay here and you fellas get into town before it's too late.'

———

Casy heard the truck coming back and got out of the Wilson's car.

'I never expected to see you so soon,' he said, as Al pulled up.

'We was lucky,' Tom said. 'We can fix her up real good.'

The three men worked together. The new con-rod was fitted in and the parts put back. Tom tightened the bolts.

Al got into the car and started the engine. It roared.

'OK,' said Tom, 'Turn her off. I think we've done it. Where's that meat now?'

The three men wiped their hands on their trousers, ate the meat and drank the water from the bottle.

'Let's get to the camp now,' Tom said. 'I'll drive her. You bring the truck, Al.'

———

There was a small wooden house on the camp ground. There were half a dozen tents near the house and cars stood beside the tents.

The owner of the ground sat on a chair in front of the house, a lamp by his side. Tom parked the car by the side of the road and walked through the gate. He saw the circle of campers standing in the light of the lamp.

'You men want to camp here?' the owner asked.

'No,' said Tom. 'We've got folks here. Hi¹, Pa.'

The owner said, 'If you want to camp here, it'll cost you half a dollar.'

'We can sleep beside the road and it won't cost nothing,' said Tom.

'We've got a law against sleeping out in this state. If the deputy sheriff⁶ comes by, you'll be in trouble.'

'He ain't your brother by any chance?' Tom asked.

'No, he ain't. And I don't have to take that kind of talk from you, either.'

'You don't have to take my half dollar either,' said Tom.

'Well, we all got to make a living,' the owner said in a quieter voice.

Pa spoke to everyone.

'We made a good living once. Had our own place till we were moved off. We ain't travelling for fun. We're going out west. We'll get good wages there.'

A thin, ragged man was staring hard at Pa. The man laughed, a high, stupid laugh, and said, 'Picking oranges maybe. Gonna pick peaches?'

'We're going to take what work they've got,' Pa said.

The ragged man laughed again.

Tom turned to him, 'What's so funny about that?'

'You folks are all going to California. Me – I'm coming back. I've been there.'

All the faces turned quickly towards him. The men's bodies were stiff and still.

'I'm going back home to starve,' the man said. 'I'd rather starve there than anywhere else.'

Pa said angrily, 'My handbill says they need men.'

'I've seen that handbill,' said the man. 'This fella wants eight hundred men. So he prints five thousand bills and maybe twenty thousand people see them.'

'But that don't make sense!' Pa cried.

'It makes sense to the fella who put out the bills. He sees people with no food. So he tells them: "I'm paying twenty cents an hour." Maybe a thousand men find out. Half the men won't do it. But the other five hundred are so hungry, they'll work for biscuits. The more fellas he can get, and the hungrier they are, the less he's got to pay.'

The ragged man looked round.

'I'm telling you folks what it took me a year to find out. And two kids and my wife dead. And me, running around, trying to get work. Not for money, just for a little food to keep them from starving.'

The ragged man turned and walked quietly into the darkness. The other men said nothing and began to move away.

Pa said, 'Was that fella telling the truth?'

'He was telling what happened to him,' said Casy.

They walked to the tent. Ma came out to meet them.

'All sleeping,' she said. 'Granma too.'

Then she saw Tom.

'You ain't had no trouble?'

'We've got the car fixed,' said Tom. 'We're ready to go early in the morning.'

'Thank God for that,' Ma said. 'I want to get there quick. I want to see all that green.'

Pa began, 'Fella down there was saying . . .' Tom grabbed his arm to stop him.

'We'll go now,' he said. 'We'll be sleeping on the right hand side of the road a little way ahead. Goodnight, Ma.'

The owner sat in his chair and watched Tom, Al and Casy walk out. They went through the gate and climbed into the car. Tom picked up a piece of earth and threw it. It hit the house and the owner jumped up, staring angrily into the darkness.

8

California

The Joads and Wilsons moved slowly westwards into the mountains of New Mexico. They climbed into the high country of Arizona.

Water was scarce now and they had to pay for it. In front of them were the high mountain peaks of Arizona.

They came to the mountains in the night. They drove all night and passed over the top. They went slowly down and when the daylight came, they saw the Colorado river below them. Over the bridge, and then they stopped.

Pa called, 'We're there – we're in California!'

'We're not in California yet,' said Tom. 'We've got to cross the desert. We've got to get to the water now, and rest.'

They sat in the cars and looked at the clear, clean water of the Colorado river. There were eleven tents near the water. They drove the cars to an empty place near the tents and got out. Winfield and Ruthie walked into the water and stood there quietly.

'We've got the desert yet,' Ruthie said.

'What's the desert like?'

'Don't know. Going to cross her at night. That's what Tom said. We'll get burned up if we go in daylight.'

The men took off their clothes near the trees, walked into the water, and sat down. They lay in the water and looked across at the white rock mountains of Arizona.

'We came through them,' said Pa in wonder.

'We've got the desert yet,' said Tom. 'Are we going to try crossing her tonight, Pa?'

'Well, I don't know. I'd like to get across her. We've only got forty dollars left. I'd like to get a job soon.'

A father and his boy walked into the water and sat down.

Pa asked politely, 'Going west?'

'No. We've come from there. Going back home. At home we can starve to death with folks we know. We won't have fellas round us that hate us.'

Pa said, 'You're the second fella I've heard talk like that. I'd like to hear some more about this.'

'Me too,' Tom said. 'Why do these folks out west hate you?

The man looked sharply at Tom.

'You ain't ever been to California?'

'No, we ain't.'

'Well, go see for yourself.'

'Yeah,' said Tom, 'but a fella wants to know.'

The man spoke carefully.

'Well, California's a nice country. It's the prettiest country you've ever seen. All orchards and grapes and water under-ground. It's good land, but it ain't yours. If you plant a little corn there, you get put in jail.

'And the people there. They look at you. And they hate you because they're scared. They're scared someone's going to take that land. You've never been called "Okie" yet.'

Tom said, '"Okie"? What's that?'

'Well, Okie used to mean you were from Oklahoma. Now it means you're no good, you're dirt. There's three hundred of our people there, living like dogs.'

Tom looked down into the water.

'But if a fella worked and saved money, couldn't he get a little land?'

'You ain't going to get steady[7] work. You're going to fight for your dinner every day.'

Pa asked slowly, 'Ain't it nice out there at all?'

'Sure, it's nice to look at, but you can't have none of it. There's a grove of yellow oranges – and a guy[1] with a gun. He'll hit you if you touch one.'

'But if a fella's willing to work hard . . .' Pa began.

The man sat up and faced him.

'Look, mister, I don't know everything. You might get out there and find a steady job.'

Tom looked at his father.

'What do you think, Pa? Are we going on tonight?'

'We might as well. Might as well get there and see for ourselves. I'm going to get some sleep.'

He stood up and the others followed him to the shore. In the water, the man and the boy watched the Joads go up to the tents.

And the boy said, 'I'd like to see them in six months.'

In the tent, the air was very hot. Granma lay on a mattress. Ma sat on the ground beside her, fanning the air with a piece of cardboard. Rose of Sharon sat on the other side watching her mother. Then the girl looked down at the old woman and said, 'She's awful[3] sick.'

Ma said, 'This here's a time of change. A time of dying. But don't you worry, Rosasharn. You're going to have a baby.'

Granma sighed, then began to breathe more deeply.

'She's asleep now,' Ma said. 'You lay down beside her and rest, Rosasharn.'

'I wonder where Connie is,' the girl complained. 'I ain't seen him for a long time.'

Ma said, 'Shh . . . Get some rest.'

Rose of Sharon closed her eyes. Ma relaxed. The camp was quiet. Then, in her half-sleep, Ma heard footsteps.

'Who's in here?'

Ma sat up quickly. A brown-faced man looked in the tent. He wore a gun and there was a big silver star[6] on his shirt.

Ma said, 'What do you want, mister?'

'Where's your men? Where're you from?'

'Near Sallisaw, Oklahoma. We're crossing the desert tonight, mister.'

'Well, you'd better. We don't want none of you Okies settling down here.'

Ma's face darkened with anger. She picked up an iron pan.

'Okies?' she said softly. 'Okies? You've got a gun, mister, but I'm not scared of you.'

The man turned.

'If you're here tomorrow, I'll take you to jail,' he said, as he walked away.

Ma kept back her tears. She put the pan back in the box.

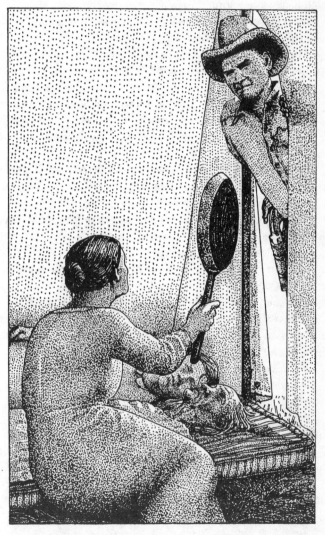

A brown-faced man looked in the tent.

The sun was lower in the sky, but it was still hot. Ma started a fire of twigs and began to heat some water. She looked up as Tom came back from a long, heavy sleep under the trees.

'I was scared, Tom,' she said. 'There was a policeman here. He talked so bad, I nearly hit him.'

'My God, Ma,' said Tom, smiling. 'First you take up a jack-handle, now you try to hit a cop[6]. What's happened to you?'

Ma looked serious. 'I don't know. Tom, this policeman, he called us Okies. He says they don't want no Okies settling down.'

Ma put some more sticks on the fire. She said, 'I pray God we're going to get some rest. I pray we're going to lay down in a nice place.'

Tom sent Ruthie down to the trees to call the men. They came up, their eyes still sleepy and heavy.

Pa said, 'What's the matter?'

'We're going,' said Tom. 'Cop says we've got to go. We've got three hundred miles to get through.'

Wilson walked up to the fire.

'We can't go, folks. Sairy's got to rest. She ain't going to get across that desert alive.'

Tom said, 'Cop says he'll jail us if we're here tomorrow.'

Wilson shook his head. 'Sairy can't go. She's got to rest and get strong. If they jail us, they jail us.'

He turned to Casy. 'Sairy wants you to go and see her.'

'Sure,' said the preacher.

The men were loading up the truck now. Everything was put away carefully. The buckets were filled with water.

Tom said, 'With this load, the engine will need plenty of water.'

Ma passed round boiled potatoes and the family ate them standing up.

Then Ma went into the Wilson tent and stayed there ten minutes. She came out quietly.

'It's time to go,' she said.

Granma was still asleep. They lifted her up on her mattress and gently put it on top of the truck.

Pa took money from his pocket and pointed to the potatoes and meat.

'We want you to take that, and this money,' he said to Wilson.

'I ain't going to,' Wilson said.

Ma took the money from Pa's hand and placed the meat pan over it.

'That's where it is,' she said. 'If you don't get it, then someone else will.'

'We've got to go,' Tom said. 'It must be nearly four.'

The family climbed on the truck. Ma was on top, beside Granma. Tom, Al and Pa sat in front and the rest were on top of the truck.

Pa called, 'Goodbye, Mister and Mrs Wilson.'

There was no answer from the tent. Tom started the engine. As they crawled up the rough road to the highway, Ma looked back. Wilson was standing in front of his tent now, staring after them. Ma waved, but he did not wave back.

In the last service station before the desert, Tom bought oil and gas and checked the old tyres. He filled the radiator with water.

The two service station men looked after the truck as it crawled away. One said, 'I'd hate to cross the desert in an old truck like that.'

'Well, them Okies ain't got no sense. They ain't human. A human being couldn't live so dirty and miserable.'

'Yeah,' said the other, 'and they're so stupid. They don't even know it's dangerous to go through the desert like that. But why worry? They ain't people like us anyway . . .'

9

Across the Desert

The truck moved up the long hill. They came to the top while the sun was still up. The yellow sun shone down on the grey desert. The black mountains and the glaring sun were straight in front of them.

Tom turned off the engine as they went down on to the flat desert. The water in the radiator cooled.

Then the sun went down and it was black dark under the cover of the truck. For a time, the people on top of the truck talked in whispers. Then at last everyone, except Ma, fell asleep. At the back of the truck, Ma sat on the mattress beside Granma. She could feel the old woman's heart beating fast.

Ma said, over and over, 'It's gonna² be all right. The family's got to get across. You know that.'

After a time, Granma was still and Ma lay down beside her.

The night hours passed. Sometimes cars passed them, going west; and sometimes big trucks rolled towards the east. It was near midnight when they reached Dagget, where the inspection station was. There were bright lights and a sign: "Keep right and stop".

An officer came out of the station.

Tom asked, 'What's this here?'

'Agricultural inspection. We've got to look over your stuff – see if you've got any vegetables or seeds. You've got to unload.'

Ma climbed down from the truck. Her eyes were hard.

'Look, mister,' she said. 'we've got a sick old lady. We've got to get her to a doctor.' She was fighting back tears.

'You can't make us wait. I swear we ain't got anything. And Granma's awful sick.'

Ma pulled herself up on to the truck.

'Look,' she said.

The officer flashed his light on the old woman's face.

'By God, she is sick. Go on ahead. You can get a doctor in the next town.'

Tom climbed in and drove on. He stopped at the town and walked round the truck.

'She's all right,' Ma said. 'Drive on. We've got to get across.'

Tom shook his head and walked back.

'I don't know what's happened to Ma,' he said to Al. 'First she says Granma's sick, then she says she's all right. I can't understand her.'

Pa said, 'Ma's almost like she was when she was a girl. She was a wild one then. She wasn't scared of nothing.'

———

Now Al was driving. He drove on steadily through the hot darkness. And the dawn light showed high mountains to the west. They filled up with oil and water at Mojave and crawled into the mountains.

Tom said, 'Jesus, the desert's past. Pa, Al, the desert's past!'

'I'm too tired to care,' said Al.

The sun came up behind them and then – suddenly – they saw the great valley below them.

Al braked and stopped in the middle of the road.

'Look!' he said.

There were the vineyards, the orchards, the great flat valley, green and beautiful. There were the farmhouses and the trees set in rows.

Pa sighed. 'I never knew anything like it.'

There were the peach trees and the orange groves. And the red roofs and barns among the trees.

Pa called. 'Ma – come look. We're there!'

Ruthie and Winfield climbed down stiffly.

51

Ruthie whispered, 'It's California!'

The others climbed down and stood beside them.

Tom said, 'Where's Ma? I want Ma to see it. Look, Ma. Come here, Ma!'

Ma was climbing down slowly. Her head was stiff. Her eyes were red and tired.

'You say we're across?' said Ma.

Tom pointed to the great valley.

Ma turned her head. 'Thank God,' she said, 'the family's here.'

Her knees bent suddenly and she sat down.

'You sick, Ma? Didn't you get no sleep?'

'No.'

'Is Granma bad?'

Ma raised her eyes and looked across the valley.

'Granma's dead.'

They looked at her, all of them, and Pa asked, 'When?'

'Before they stopped us last night.'

'So that's why you didn't want them to look,' said Tom.

'I was afraid we wouldn't get across,' Ma said. 'I told Granma we couldn't help her. We couldn't stop in the desert. We had to think of the young ones and Rosasharn's baby!'

Ma put her head in her hands and covered her face for a moment.

'She can get buried in a nice green place,' Ma said.

The family looked at Ma, a little afraid of her strength.

Tom said, 'Jesus Christ, you lay there with her all night long!'

He moved to put his hand on her shoulder.

'Don't touch me,' Ma said. 'Can I sit up front now? I don't want to go back there no more. I'm awful tired.'

The others climbed back on the truck, keeping away from the stiff, covered figure.

Ruth whispered, 'That's Granma, and she's dead.'

Ruthie whispered, 'It's California!'

Tom and Ma and Pa got into the front seat. The heavy truck rolled towards the green and golden valley.

'It's pretty,' said Ma. 'I wish they could have seen it.'

The truck followed the twisting road down the mountains. Tom said, 'I guess we've got to go to the coroner[6], wherever he is. We've got to get her buried nicely. How much money's left, Pa?'

'About thirty dollars,' said Pa.

Tom laughed. 'We sure ain't bringing nothing with us!'

He laughed for a moment. Then his face became serious and he pulled his cap down over his eyes.

And the truck rolled down the mountain into the green valley.

10

The Making of California

Long ago, California had belonged to the Mexicans. Then the Americans had come, hungry for land. The Americans stole the land and guarded what they had stolen with guns. The Mexicans were too weak to fight back. And so the Americans lived on the land and had children. They had become the owners of the land.

After a time, they forgot about their first hungry need for the land. They no longer loved the land; they loved money. Farmers became shopkeepers, and then business men. And these business men owned the land, but they did not know it. Many of these men had never seen the land they owned. They had never seen the crops they grew.

Then the small farmers from Kansas, Texas and Oklahoma

lost their land and came out west. Homeless and hungry, two hundred thousand, and then many more, came over the mountains.

They were hungry and they were fierce. They had hoped to find a home, and they had found only hatred. Okies – the owners hated them. The owners were soft and the Okies were strong. The owners were well-fed and the Okies were hungry.

The shopkeepers hated the Okies too, because they had no money to spend. The Okies wanted only two things – land and food. And the Californians hated them for it.

The hungry men drove their cars through the orange groves. Men were standing there with guns. The children were starving, but they could not eat the oranges. The hungry men had no money. They could get no work. Where could their families sleep at night?

The Okies were forced to stay in tents, outside the towns and close to water. Sometimes they made houses from paper and cardboard. During the day, the men looked for work and did not find it. At night they sat together talking. These men were not armed, but they were dangerous. They knew what they wanted and the Californians were afraid of them.

So the Californians burnt the Okies' camps.

'These camps of yours are dangerous,' the Californians said. 'They spread disease. We've got orders to get you out of here. In half an hour, we'll set fire to the camp.'

In half an hour, the people were on the road again, looking for another camp. And still, in Oklahoma, in Kansas and in Texas, the tractors were pushing the people out. There were three hundred thousand migrants in California and more were coming.

The Californian landowners were afraid that the three hundred thousand might find a leader. They used every way they could to destroy the migrants. They knew that one day the migrants would stop talking, would stop praying to God to feed their children. The migrants would fight back. And that would be the end.

11

Looking for Work

In Bakersfield, the next town, Pa and Ma went into the coroner's office. Then the long bundle was lifted down from the truck and taken inside. The rest of the family stayed in the truck, out in the heat.

Very soon, Pa and Ma came out.

Ma said, 'Well, we've done the best we could for Granma. Got her buried nicely. Now we've got to get on. We've got to find a place to stay. Get work and settle down.'

'Where are we going?' Tom asked.

'Camp,' said Pa. 'Drive out in the country.'

By a bridge, outside the town, they found the camp – a collection of about forty tents and cardboard houses. Beside each living-place was some kind of truck or car.

Tom stopped the truck and looked at Pa.

'It ain't very pretty,' he said. 'Want to go somewhere else?'

'Can't go nowhere else. Got to ask about work first,' said Pa.

'Let's get the tent up,' said Ma. 'I'm tired out. Maybe we can all rest.'

Tom helped Pa and the other men to lift the cover onto the tent poles. A circle of quiet children watched the new family get settled.

Tom walked across to a young man who was mending a car. Tom looked at the dirty tents, the blackened cooking pans and the old cars.

'Ain't there no work?' Tom asked.

'Ain't no crop here, right now. Grapes to pick later and cotton to pick after that.'

Tom said, 'Back home, some fellas gave out handbills. Says they need lots of people out here to pick the crops.'

The young man laughed.

'They say there's three hundred thousand out here and they've all seen those handbills.'

'But if they don't need folks,' said Tom, 'why do they put out those handbills?'

'Look,' the young man said, 'if you've got a job of work and just one fella wants the job, you've got to pay him what he asks. But if there's a hundred men, and those men have got kids, those men'll fight to work. Last job I had, they were paying fifteen cents an hour. And you had to use gas getting there. That's how it is.'

'But I've seen all the stuff growing,' said Tom. 'It's got to be picked!'

'Right. Take peaches,' the young man said. 'They need three thousand men for two weeks when those peaches are ripe. So you pick and pick and then it's finished. Then they don't want you around. so they kick you out, they move you along. That's how it is.'

Tom said angrily, 'But if the people said, "Let those peaches rot", they'd have to put up the wage then, wouldn't they?'

The young man smiled. 'Folks thought of that. But those folks had to have a leader, to do the talking. Well, the first time that fella opened his mouth, they grabbed him and put him in jail.'

Tom took off his cap and twisted it in his hands.

'So we take what we can get, or we starve; and if we shout about it, we starve too,' he said.

'Yeah,' the young man answered. 'And when the cops come round, act stupid. You're a stupid Okie, remember that.'

———

Inside the tent, Rose of Sharon lay on a mattress and her husband, Connie, sat beside her. Connie's eyes were dark and angry.

'If I'd known it would be like this, I wouldn't have come,'

he said. 'I could've studied about tractors. I could've got three dollars a day driving a tractor.'

Rose of Sharon looked worried.

'You're going to study about radios. You got to! We got to have a home before the baby comes. We ain't going to have this baby in a tent.'

'Sure,' he said. 'I'm going to study. But it would be better to have stayed at home maybe, and studied about tractors.'

He went out of the tent. Rose of Sharon rolled on her back and cried silently.

The children standing around Ma's fire could smell the stew in the pot now.

'I could break up sticks if you want, ma'am,' one little girl said politely. Ma looked up from her work.

'You want to get asked to eat, huh?'

'Yes, ma'am,' said the little girl.

Ma looked hard at the little girl. 'How long have your folks been in California?' Ma asked.

'Oh, about six months. We lived in a government camp for a while. Then we went north and when we came back, the government camp was full. That's a real nice place, ma'am.'

'Where is it?' Ma asked.

'Over by Weedpatch. Got nice toilets and baths. You can wash clothes in a tub. There's music, and on Saturday night, folks give a dance. I wish we could live there again.'

'It must cost a lot,' said Ma.

'Well, it costs, but if you ain't got money, you work.'

Ma said, 'I sure wish we could go there.'

Al walked up to the young man who was mending the car.

'I talked to a fella a while ago,' said the younger man. 'He's with you ain't he?'

'Yeah, that's my brother, Tom. You'd better not fool with him. He once killed a fella.'

'He don't look like a fighter.'

'He ain't. Tom, he's quiet, but he don't let nobody fool with him.'

Al looked at the inside of the old engine.

'Would you like me to help you?' he said. 'I can't keep my hands out of a car engine.'

'Thanks,' the young man said. 'I'd like that. I'm Floyd Knowles.'

'I'm Al Joad.'

'I've been here six months,' Floyd said. 'I've been looking all over for work. As soon as we get this car fixed, we're going to move. There's work up north.'

'Al!'

Al looked down at Winfield, standing importantly beside him.

'Al, Ma's dishing up the stew. She says come and get it.'

'Right,' said Al. 'We ain't ate today,' he told Floyd. 'I'll help you later.'

Ma looked up helplessly as Al came up. There was a circle of strange children standing round the fire and the stewpot.

Ma said, 'I don't know what to do. I've got to feed the family. What am I going to do with all these kids?'

Tom spoke to the children. 'You get away now,' he said. 'There ain't enough for you.'

Ma put a very little stew on to tin plates for the family.

'There's not much,' she said. 'Take your plates and go into the tent. I'll let these kids scrape the pot.'

The children ran for flat sticks or spoons. Ma went into the tent. From inside the tent the family could hear the children scraping the pot. The pot was left empty on the ground.

'Can't do that no more,' Ma said. 'We've got to eat alone.'

Al got to his feet. 'Got to help a fellow with a car,' he said. In a few minutes, he was back.

'Tom,' Al shouted outside the tent, 'come along with me.' He led Tom to the old car.

There was a circle of strange children standing round the fire and the stewpot.

'This here is Floyd Knowles,' he said. 'Tell him, Floyd.'

Floyd said, 'There's going to be work up north.'

'Yeah, what kind of work? How far?' Tom asked.

'Pear picking. Maybe two hundred miles away.'

Tom said sadly, 'I hoped we could get work here and rent a house to live in.'

Floyd said carefully, 'There's things you've got to learn. You ain't going to settle down, 'cause[2] there ain't no work for you.'

'We'd better go and see, Tom,' Al said. 'By God, I think I'll go if the family goes or not.'

'Ma ain't going to like that,' Tom said.

The three young men bent over the car engine and worked on in silence.

A big new car drew off the highway and stopped in the centre of the camp.

'Who's this?' Tom said.

'Cops, maybe,' said Floyd.

The three men put down their tools and walked towards the car. A man was getting out.

'You men want to work?' he said.

Men from all over the camp moved near.

'Sure we want work. Where is it?'

'Tulare County. We need a lot of fruit pickers.'

'What're you paying?' Floyd asked.

'Maybe thirty cents an hour.'

'Why can't you tell for sure?' asked Floyd. 'You've got the contract[5], haven't you?'

'The pay might be a little more, might be a little less.'

Floyd stepped forward. He said quietly, 'I'll go, mister. You show me your licence to hire[5] men. Tell us our pay, and how many men you need, and I'll go.'

The man said, 'Are you telling me how to run my business? I don't know those things. All I know is, I need men. Going to need a lot of men.'

Floyd turned to the crowd of men.

'Twice before I've believed that talk,' he said. 'Maybe he needs a thousand men. He'll get five thousand there and he'll pay fifteen cents an hour. And we'll have to take it, 'cause we'll be hungry. Ask to see his licence.'

The contractor[5] turned to the car and shouted, 'Joe!'

A heavily-built man got out. He wore a deputy sheriff's star and carried a heavy gun.

The contractor pointed to Floyd.

'Ever seen this fella before, Joe? He's talking red[1], causing trouble.'

The heavy man looked hard at Floyd.

'Yeah, I've seen him around. Near that car robbery. Yeah, I'm sure it's the same fella. Get in that car, you!'

Tom said, 'What's he done wrong?'

'If you say any more, you'll be in the car too,' the deputy replied. He looked round at all the men.

'This contractor can use all of you. Tulare County. It might be a good idea to go. This camp's dirty. We've got to clean it out. We might have to do a lot of burning. Might be better if you're not here when we do that. There's plenty of work in Tulare. I don't want any of you here by tomorrow morning. Now, you,' the deputy said to Floyd, 'you get in that car.'

As he took hold of Floyd's left arm, Floyd's right fist hit the man's large face. Floyd turned to run, and as the deputy went after him, Tom put out his foot and tripped him up. The deputy fired his gun as he lay on the ground.

A woman screamed. Blood poured from her torn fingers. The deputy raised his gun again. Casy stepped from the crowd and kicked the deputy in the neck. He fell back unconscious.

The car with the contractor roared away. The woman began to scream, louder and louder. Tom picked up the deputy's gun, unloaded it, and threw it into the bushes.

Casy moved closer to Tom.

'You've got to get out,' Casy said. 'The cop saw you put out your foot. Don't forget, you've broken parole. They'll send you back to jail.'

Tom drew in his breath sharply. 'Jesus, I forgot,' he said.

He walked away, hurrying into the trees.

In the distance, there was the scream of a police car siren. At once, the men were nervous. They moved away into their tents. Only Al and Casy were left. Casy turned to Al.

'Go on,' he said. 'Get into the tent. You don't know nothing.'

'Yeah? How about you?'

Casy smiled at him. 'Somebody's got to take the blame. I ain't got no kids. If you get into trouble, they'll find out about Tom and send him to jail.'

Al thought for a moment.

'OK,' he said, 'but you're a fool, Casy.'

The siren screamed again. It was coming nearer. The men were all in their tents now. Casy knelt by the deputy and turned him over.

Four men with rifles got out of the police car.

'What the hell's⁴ going on here?'

'I knocked out your man there,' said Casy. 'He started shooting – hit a woman, so I hit him.'

'Get in that car.'

'Sure,' said Casy.

The deputy sat up and stared at Casy. 'He don't look like the right fella to me.'

'It was me all right,' Casy said. 'I'll go without trouble. You'd better help that woman.'

Casy climbed into the back seat of the police car.

After a time, the people in the tents heard the car start up. Then they came out of their tents again. Al crawled out of the Joads' tent and went to get Tom.

'Now what the hell made the preacher do that?' Pa asked.

12

'We're the People . . .'

The sun was down now, but, to the east, the mountains were still yellow with sunlight.

Pa watched Ma build her little fire. She peeled potatoes and sliced them into a pan. Behind them, Rose of Sharon moved slowly out of the tent.

'Where's Connie?' she said. 'I ain't feeling good. Connie shouldn't leave me alone.'

Ma looked up at the girl's sad face.

'You've been crying,' she said. 'Come here now and peel potatoes. You've got to stop feeling sorry for yourself.'

Rose of Sharon came slowly towards the fire.

'He shouldn't have left me alone,' she repeated. She took up the knife. 'Wait till I see him,' she said fiercely.

Ma smiled slowly. 'He might beat you. If he beats some sense into you, I'll thank him. Now stop feeling sorry for yourself.'

The girl's eyes were angry, but she said nothing. Al and Tom came up talking quietly. Tom said, 'Casy shouldn't have done it. But he's been talking all the time about how he wanted to do something for us.'

'Where do you think Connie was going when we saw him out there just now?' asked Al.

'I don't know. But he was going away from the camp fast.'

Floyd called to Tom and Al quietly from his tent.

'You getting out?' he asked them.

Tom said, 'I don't know. Do you think we'd better?'

Floyd laughed. 'You heard what the cops said. They'll be back to burn us out tonight, for sure.'

Al said, 'Where's that government camp that little girl talked about?'

'Go south on Highway 99 about twelve or fourteen miles. Then turn east to Weedpatch. But I think the camp's full up.'

'We'll try it,' said Tom. 'So long, Floyd.'

'Goodbye,' said Al. They walked through the dark to the Joad tent.

'It's Tom!' Ma cried. 'Thank God!'

'We've got to get out of here,' Tom said. 'They'll burn the camp tonight. Those cops want to push us along.'

Rose of Sharon said, 'Have you seen Connie?'

'Yeah,' said Al. 'He's a long way off. Going south.'

Ma looked hard at the girl.

'What did Connie say to you?' she asked.

'He said it would have been better if he'd stayed at home and learnt to drive a tractor.'

They were very quiet. The potatoes hissed in the pan.

Pa said, 'Connie weren't³ no good. I've known that a long time.'

Rose of Sharon got up. She went into the tent and lay down covering her face with her hands.

'It wouldn't do no good to bring Connie back, I guess,' Al said.

Pa replied, 'No, he ain't no good. He's run out and we don't want him.'

Ma said, 'Don't say that. Rosasharn's going to have a little baby and that baby is half Connie. Say Connie's dead and don't say no bad things about him.'

Tom said, 'We ain't sure Connie's left us. But we've no time for talking. We've got to eat and get on our way.'

'On our way? We've just come here,' Ma said. Tom explained.

'Then come on,' Ma cried. 'Let's eat this stuff and go quick.'

They ate the hot potatoes, then, without a word, began to load the truck. Rosasharn sat away from the others, watching, and then said, 'I want Connie. I ain't going till he comes back.'

Cars started up as other families left the camp. Ma came up and stood beside her daughter.

'Come on Rosasharn. Come on, honey[1].'

'I want to wait.'

'We can't wait.' Ma leant down and helped the girl to her feet. 'He'll find us. Don't you worry. He'll find us.'

'Maybe he went to get some books to study,' said Rose of Sharon. 'Maybe he was going to surprise us.'

Ma said, 'Maybe that's what he's done.' They led the girl to the truck and helped her up on top of the load.

'Come on, Pa, let's go,' Tom said. 'Al, you get up behind. Take this wrench. If anyone climbs up, hit him.'

Tom put the jack-handle on the floor beside him. He started the truck and they climbed up to the highway and turned south.

'Be careful, Tom,' Ma said. 'The family's breaking up. You've got to take care.'

The truck crawled along. There was a little row of red lights across the road in front of them. Tom slowed down and then stopped the truck. Immediately it was surrounded by a group of men with pick handles and shot guns. One man leant in the window.

'Where do you think you're going?' he asked. His breath smelt of whisky and his face was red. Tom's hand went down to the floor to pick up the jack-handle. Ma caught his arm and held it.

'Well,' Tom said slowly, 'we're strangers here. We heard there's work in a place called Tulare. We ain't doing no harm, mister.'

'You're going the wrong way. We don't want no Okies in this town.'

Tom's body was stiff with anger, but he spoke softly.

'Which way do we go, mister?'

One man leant in the window.

'You turn right around and go north. And don't come back here till the cotton's ready.'

Tom shivered. 'Yes, sir,' he said. He turned the truck and went back the way they had come. Ma patted his arm. And Tom tried to stop his tears of anger.

'Don't you worry about them,' Ma said. 'You done good[3].' Tom turned on to a side road, went a hundred yards and turned off the lights and engine.

'Where're you going?' Ma demanded.

'Just going to look. We ain't going north.'

In a few moments there came the sounds of shouts and screams. A light flared up from the direction of their old camp. The light grew brighter and they could hear a crackling sound. The camp was on fire. Tom got into the truck again. At the highway, he turned south.

'Where're we going, Tom?' Ma asked.

'Going south,' Tom answered. 'But I'll try to get around the town, not through it. I'm going to look for that government camp. There's no deputies there. Ma – if I see one of those fellas again, I'm going to kill him.'

'Take it easy[7],' Ma said. 'You've got to have patience.'

'It ain't easy to be patient all the time,' Tom said.

'I know,' Ma laughed quietly. 'That's what makes us tough. They ain't going to stop us. Don't you worry, Tom. There's a different time coming. Things'll get better. I know they will.'

Tom turned for a second to look at his mother. Her face was quiet and there was a strange look in her eyes. Tom touched her gently on the shoulder.

'Never heard you talk so much in my life,' he said.

'I never had so much reason for talking,' Ma said.

Tom drove through the side streets of the town and found a sign: "99". He turned south on the highway.

'Well, they never made us go north,' he said. 'We still go where we want, even if we've got to crawl.'

The truck's lights shone on the black highway in front of them.

———

The moving people were migrants now. Those families who had lived and died on forty acres of land, now moved over the whole west. They looked for work. More families came after them.

In the west, the landowners were afraid. 'These Okies are thieves,' they said. 'They're stupid and dirty. We hate them. We must stop them taking our land.'

The migrants fought to work. They took low wages to get a job. Wages went down and the prices went up.

And then the owners were glad. They sent out more handbills to bring more people in. And the highways were crowded with hungry men, desperate for work.

The crops were good, and yet these people and their children starved. The landowners did not understand that hungry people can soon become angry people.

On the highways, the people moved like ants and searched for work, for food. And the anger began to grow.

13

The Government Camp

It was very late and completely dark now. Tom Joad drove slowly along the country road, looking for Weedpatch Camp.

Tom said to Pa, 'I don't know where the camp is. Maybe we'll wait for daylight and ask somebody.'

A few hundred yards later he saw the camp. A high wire fence faced the road. Tom turned into the wide driveway. A man came out of a small house with a light in the window.

Tom leant out of the truck: 'Have you got any room for us?'

'How many of you?'

Tom counted on his fingers: 'Me and Pa and Ma. Al and Rosasharn and Ruthie and Winfield. The last two are only kids.'

'Well, I guess we can have you. Drive down the end of that line and turn right. You'll be in Number Four Sanitary Unit.'

'What's that?'

'Toilets and showers and wash-tubs.'

Ma demanded, 'You got wash-tubs, running water?'

'Sure.'

'Oh, praise God,' said Ma.

Tom drove down the long dark row of tents.

'Pull in here,' the watchman said. 'Let the others unload and we'll fill in the papers.'

Tom left the others, climbed the office steps to a living room containing a desk and a chair. The watchman sat down and took out a form.

'Name?'

'Tom Joad.'

'That your father out there?'

'Yeah. He's Tom Joad, too.'

'Got any money? The camp site costs a dollar a week. But if you've no money, you can help clean the camp.'

'We'll do that,' Tom said.

'You'll see the committee[5] tomorrow. They'll tell you the rules.'

Tom said, 'Committee? Rules? Are they cops?'

'No, fellas like you camping here. We vote them in and we can vote them out too. No cops come in here without a warrant[6]. Then there's a Ladies' committee. They'll come and see your Ma.

And every Saturday night we have a dance. Best dances in the county.'

'Ma's going to like this place,' said Tom. 'She ain't been treated nicely for a long time.'

'Get some sleep now,' the watchman said. 'This camp wakes up early.'

Tom walked slowly back to the truck. The rows of tents were straight and there was no dirt. The Joad tent was up and all was quiet.

Ma said softly, 'That you Tom? Is it all right?'

'Everything's fine. You get some sleep now, Ma. I'll tell you about it in the morning.'

'Goodnight,' Ma said softly. Tom climbed up into the truck. He lay down on his back and looked up at the stars, clear and sharp over his head.

———

It was still dark when Tom woke up. The eastern mountains were black and, as he watched, the light came up behind them. He got down from the truck.

Beside a tent, he saw the fire burning in an old black stove. Tom moved slowly towards the stove where a girl was cooking breakfast. He smelt frying bacon and baking bread.

Two men, one old and one young, came out of the tent and saw Tom.

'Morning,' they said.

The girl worked quietly. She laid bacon on a plate and took out the bread from the oven. The older man said to Tom, 'Had your breakfast?'

'Well no, I ain't. My folks are still sleeping. We came late last night.'

'Well, sit down with us then. We've got plenty, thank God.'

71

The girl filled their plates and poured out coffee.

'We've had twelve days' work,' the young man said. 'Got ourselves new clothes. We've been eating good for twelve days.'

It was light now. The two men finished eating and stood up.

'Got to get going,' the older man said.

'Look,' said the younger man. 'We've got work. Walk over with us. Maybe we could get you work too.'

Tom said, 'That's mighty[3] nice of you. Just a minute. I'll tell my folks.'

Ruthie was awake when Tom looked into the tent. She crawled out and stood up.

'Listen here,' Tom said. 'Tell them I got a chance of a job. Tell Ma I ate breakfast with some neighbours. Don't wake her up now.'

Ruthie nodded.

———

The camp had begun to come to life. Women worked at the new fires.

'It ain't far to walk,' the older man told Tom. 'We had to sell our car. This is a good job though. We're getting thirty cents an hour.'

The three men walked off the highway, through a small orchard to a white house. A red-faced man came out.

'Morning, Mr Thomas,' the older man said. 'This here's a friend of ours. Is there work for him too?'

The red-faced man frowned.

'Oh, sure! I'll give him work. I'll give anybody work. But this morning, you ain't getting thirty cents an hour – you're getting twenty-five. It's not me. The Farmers' Association[5] told me last night the rate's[5] twenty-five. If I don't pay less, I won't get a bank loan[5] next year.'

72

The men looked at the ground. 'We'll work,' they said.

Tom said, 'Sure I'll work. I've got to work.'

Thomas looked at his watch. 'Well, let's get started,' he said. He looked up.

'I'm going to tell you something. But don't ever say I told you. Take care at your dance next Saturday night. There's going to be a fight in the camp on Saturday. Some fellas are going to break in and make trouble. The deputies will be ready to go in and break up the camp.'

'Why, for God's sake . . .?' said Tom. 'These folks aren't giving any trouble to anybody.'

'I'll tell you why,' Thomas said. 'People here say that the folks in your camp are living too well. When they go back to those other camps, they'll cause trouble. Go on out to work now. I hope I haven't said too much. But I like you people.'

The men took picks and shovels from the barn and began to work.

Tom held the pick. 'Sweet Jesus[4], this feels good.'

He lifted the pick and started work. The sweat rolled down from his forehead on to his neck.

———

In front of the tent Ma stood, looking up and down. Al and Rosasharn and Pa were still asleep. Winfield and Ruthie came running up.

'I was worrying,' Ma said when she saw them. 'Didn't know where you'd gone. You seen Tom?'

Ruth said importantly, 'Tom told me to tell you. He's got work. Went out of the camp to work.'

Ma reached out for Ruthie and hugged her.

'They've got toilets over there,' Ruthie said pointing to the Sanitary Unit. 'I've been there.'

The children walked away and Ma was left alone.

She went to the unit building, and looked inside. The toilets lined one side of the large room and each toilet had its compartment with a door in front of it. Hand basins lined another wall and on the third wall, there were four shower compartments. Everything was clean and white.

She turned on the water in one of the basins. When the water ran hot, she pulled her finger away.

She looked at the basin, put in the plug and turned on hot and cold water. Ma washed her face and hands and put water on her hair.

She heard a sound and turned. A man stood behind her. He said angrily, 'What are you doing here?'

Ma looked at him. 'I thought this was here for folks to use,' she said.

The man frowned. 'For menfolks,' he said and pointed to the sign on the door: "MEN".

'I never seen that,' said Ma. 'Ain't there a place where I can go?'

The man smiled. 'Have you just come?' he said.

'In the middle of the night.'

'Then you ain't seen the Ladies' Committee. They'll be around to tell you everything. The ladies' toilet is on the other side of the building.'

'Why, thank you,' said Ma and hurried back to the tent.

'Pa,' she said, 'get up! You, Al, get up and get washed. All of you,' Ma cried.

Pa asked, 'What's the matter?'

'There's a Ladies' Committee coming to visit us. We got to get washed and get breakfast over.' Ma started a fire.

'Quick, we've got to be quick,' she said to herself.

Rose of Sharon crawled sleepily out of the tent.

'Go right over there and clean up,' Ma said. 'Put on a clean dress. Get your hair combed.' Ma was excited now.

'What are you doing here?'

Rose of Sharon said, 'I don't feel good. I don't feel like doing nothing without Connie.'

Ma turned. 'Rosasharn,' she said angrily, 'you stop feeling sorry for yourself.'

'But I don't feel good. I'm going to be sick.'

'Wash yourself and you'll feel better. Put on your shoes and comb your hair.'

Pa came back. 'Tom's got work,' Ma told him. 'Get yourself clean clothes from that box, Pa. Then take Ruthie and Winfield to that hot water and clean them up real good. I'm busy.'

Ma went back to her cooking. There was a smell of frying fat and of strong coffee.

Pa came back with the children. Their faces were red and shining.

'They look nice,' Ma said. 'Food's ready. Help yourself, Pa.'

Al came up excitedly. 'What a place!' he said. 'We'll go out looking for work after breakfast. 'I'll have to get gas.'

Rose of Sharon came back. Her hair was wet and neatly combed. Her skin was bright and pink. She had put on a blue dress with little white flowers. On her feet, she wore her wedding shoes.

'You had a bath?' Ma asked.

Rose of Sharon nodded.

'I'm going to have one myself when I've finished here,' Ma said. 'You can show me how.'

'I'm going to do it everyday,' Rose of Sharon said. 'A lady told me a nurse comes every week. The nurse'll tell me what to do so the baby'll be strong. And do you know what? There was a baby born last week, and they gave it a party and had a cake!'

Ma said, 'Praise God, we've come home to our own people. These folks is our folks.'

Ma went into the tent and found herself a clean dress. 'If them ladies come, tell them I'll be right back,' she said.

Rose of Sharon sat down heavily on a box and looked at her black shoes. She put her hands on her stomach and smiled a secret smile.

When Ma came back, she wore her clean dress and old cracked shoes. And little earrings hung in her ears.

'I done it,' she said. 'I stood in there and let warm water flow over me.' She looked around.

'You've been sitting here doing nothing! Come on! We've got to get things ready. Get them beds neat,' she ordered Rose of Sharon.

The girl stood up slowly.

'You think Connie's coming back today?' she asked Ma.

'Maybe, maybe not. Can't tell. He'll come back when he comes. Now get to work. Here's the ladies coming. Get to work so I can be proud of you.'

When the committee had left, Ma sat down on a box in front of the Joad tent.

'Well,' she said. 'Wasn't them ladies nice?'

'I can work in the nursery[7],' Rose of Sharon said. 'I can find out what to do for babies. Then I'll know.'

Ma nodded. 'Wouldn't it be nice if the menfolks all got work?' she asked. 'Them working, and us working here, and all them nice people . . .'

———

With Pa beside him, Al drove the truck along the beautiful roads, past orchards and past vineyards. At each entrance gate Al slowed down; and at each gate there was a sign: "NO HELP WANTED. NO TRESPASSING".

Al said, 'Pa, there'll be work when the fruit's ready. I wish I could get work in a garage. I'd like that. Let's go back to the camp and ask where there's work. We're using too much gas.'

They drove back to the camp in silence.

Pa found Ma sitting outside the tent.

'Get work?' she asked him.

'No,' Pa said. 'We looked, but there wasn't any.'

Ma said sadly, 'This here's a nice place. We could be happy here.'

'If we could get work,' Pa said.

'Yeah! If you could get work,' said Ma. 'All the time we was[3] moving, I never thought about nothing. And now all these folks have been nice, I start thinking of the sad things. About the night Grampa died, and then about Granma . . .'

'But Tom's got work and he'll come back this evening,' said Pa.

Ma smiled.

'Ain't he a fine boy!' she said. 'Ain't he a good boy! Now, Pa, you get to the store. I want beans and sugar and a piece of meat and carrots . . . Get something nice for tonight, Pa. Tonight we'll have something nice!'

14

The Dance

On Saturday morning, the women were working at the wash-tubs. They washed dresses and hung them in the sun. By afternoon, the camp was full of life. Men were busy working at the big open-air dance platform. Everybody was excited.

By seven, dinner was over and the men were in their best clothes. The girls were ready in their bright cotton dresses, their hair smooth and tied with ribbons.

The Central Committee were having a meeting in one of the

huts. There were five men there and the chairman was speaking.

'It's lucky we were told that there's going to be trouble at the dance,' he said.

'What if somebody tries to get in by climbing over the fence?' one of the men asked.

'Well, we got twenty-five good strong men. They're going to be dancing and looking out for any trouble. At the first sign of trouble, they'll move in together and get the troublemakers out. And we've got five men on the gate, looking carefully at the people as they come in.'

'We don't want anyone to get hurt,' the chairman said. 'If there's any fighting, the deputies will move in.'

Now it was getting dark and the lights around the dance platform were on. The people came out of their tents. The guests began to arrive in their cars, small farmers and migrants from other camps. At the gate, each guest gave the name of the camper who had invited him.

Al smiled at himself in the mirror. He walked out towards the platform, his eyes open for pretty girls.

Tom finished his last mouthful of dinner.

'Ain't you going to the dance?' Ma asked.

'Sure,' said Tom. 'I'm on a committee. I've got to look over the people as they come in the gate.'

'There ain't going to be no trouble?' asked Ma.

'None at all,' said Tom. 'Well, I must go now. See you at the dance, Ma.'

Ma finished washing the dishes. Then she called into the tent.

'Rosasharn, you come out. Ain't you going to the dance?'

The girl stepped from the tent.

'I was, but I don't know. I feel folks looking at me now I'm getting so big. I wish Connie was here.'

Ma stood in front of her daughter and put her two hands on Rose of Sharon's hair.

'You're a good girl,' Ma said. 'I'll take care of you. We're going

79

to that dance and we're going to sit and watch. In a little while, things won't be so bad. And that's true.'

———

Tom stood at the gate and watched the people coming into the dance. He watched the farm families come in, and the migrants from the camps. Tom spoke to the young man beside him.

'Our people have got nothing. But because they can ask people to the dance, it makes them proud and happy again.'

'Hey, look!' the young man said suddenly.

Three young men were coming in the gate. They spoke to the guard and he let them through.

The young man went over and asked the guard, 'Who asked them three?'

'A fella called Jackson, Unit Four.'

The young man came back to Tom.

'I think those fellas are here to cause trouble. You follow them. I'll get Jackson from Unit Four.'

In a few minutes the young man came back with Jackson.

'Look, Jackson, did you ask them fellas?' said Tom.

'No.'

'Ever seen them before?'

'Sure,' said Jackson. 'I've worked with them. That's how they know my name.'

'Thanks, Mr Jackson. I guess they're the troublemakers. I'll point them out to all our men.'

A sixteen-year-old boy came running through the crowd.

'Hey,' he said. 'There's a car with six men parked down by the trees outside the fence. And there's one with four men up the road. They've got guns, I saw them.'

———

Now it was time for the dancing to begin. Boys and girls, young men and women stood on the dance floor, ready and waiting.

The music started and the dancing began. The dancers moved faster and faster. Now the girls' hair was untidy, now sweat came out on the foreheads of the boys. And the old people on the edge of the floor clapped their hands and tapped their feet.

Ma smiled. 'It makes me think of old times,' she said to Rose of Sharon. 'Your Pa was a nice dancer when he was younger.'

Then suddenly the music stopped. The first dance was over. The dancers stood still while the children rushed out onto the floor, chasing each other madly. The members of the band got up, stretched themselves and sat down again.

New dancers came forward for partners[7]. Tom stood near the three young men. He saw them push their way onto the dance floor. Twenty young men walked slowly on to the floor and watched them.

One of the three strangers said, 'I'll dance with this girl here.'

A boy looked up in surprise. 'She's my partner . . .'

'Listen here, you . . .'

In the darkness outside the camp, a whistle sounded. On the dance floor the three strangers were quietly surrounded and held firmly. They were moved off the platform. The music started and the dancing began again.

A car drove up to the entrance gate.

'Open up!' the driver called. 'We hear you've got trouble.'

The guard did not move.

'We've got no trouble,' he said. 'Listen to that music. Who are you?'

'Deputy sheriffs.'

'Got a warrant?'

'We don't need a warrant if there's trouble.'

'Well, we've got no trouble here,' the guard repeated.

The car moved slowly up the road and stopped. In the darkness, behind the dance platform, the three young men were held tightly.

*In the darkness, behind the dance platform, the three young
men were held tightly.*

'These the troublemakers? Let's look at them,' said the chairman of the committee.

The prisoners kept their heads down.

'What do you want to do it for?' the chairman went on. 'Who told you to cause trouble?' He waited for a reply.

'You're our own folks,' he continued. 'You belong with us. Who told you to break up our dance?'

'Well, a fella's got to eat,' said one of the strangers.

'Well, who sent you? Who paid you to come in here?'

'We ain't been paid.'

'I see. No fight, no pay. Ain't that right?'

One of the three said. 'Do what you want with us. We ain't telling you nothing.'

'Now listen carefully you three,' said the chairman. 'This time you're lucky. We're letting you go. But if we ever see you here again, we'll give you a hell of a beating. All right, boys. Throw these three men over the back fence.'

And on the dance floor, the band began a new tune.

15

Another Camp

On an evening when clouds covered the setting sun, the Joad family sat together in Weedpatch Camp. They had finished supper and Ma had started to do the dishes.

'We've got to do something,' Ma said suddenly. She pointed to Winfield.

'Look at him. He can't sleep good. He's not well. We've been here one month,' Ma went on, 'and Tom's had five days' work. No one else has got work at all. We've got enough food for one more day. None of you get up till we decide what to do.'

They looked at the ground. Pa cleaned his thick nails with his knife.

Ma said fiercely, 'What's happening to this here family?'

'I guess we've got to go,' said Pa. 'Don't want to. It's nice here and the folks are nice. But we've got to eat.'

'I've got a tankful of gas in the truck,' Al said. 'That'll take us somewhere.'

Ma said, 'I ain't watching this family starve no more. Rosasharn's gonna have her baby soon. She's got to be fed.'

'But the hot water and toilets here . . .' Pa began.

'Well, we can't eat no toilets,' said Ma.

Al said, 'A fella told me there's cotton to be picked maybe. Up north. Ain't very far.'

'Well, we've got to get going, and quick,' Ma told them.

'When?' asked Tom.

'We've got to go in the morning,' replied Ma. 'I've told you what's left.'

Pa made an angry noise. 'Times have changed,' he said. 'Once the man decided what to do. Women are doing the deciding now.'

Pa got up and angrily walked away.

Ma said proudly to Tom, 'He's all right. If you can make a worried man angry, he'll be all right.'

Tom said, 'I'm getting tired, Ma. How about making me angry?'

'I don't need to make you angry,' said Ma. 'You'll never give up, Tom.'

'I'm going to see to the truck, now,' said Tom, and he walked away.

Rosasharn had sat quietly while they talked. Now she got slowly to her feet.

'You feeling all right?' Ma asked her.

'I ain't had no milk.'

'I know. We didn't have no milk.'

Rose of Sharon said, 'If Connie hadn't gone away, we'd've had a little house by now. And milk. This baby ain't going to be no good without milk.'

'Don't you say that about the baby,' Ma said. 'Don't even think about it.'

'Got no husband. Got no milk.'

Ma said, 'If you were well, I'd hit you hard across the face.' She got up and went inside the tent. She came out and held out her hand. There were the small gold earrings.

'Look,' said Ma, 'these are for you. Here, you keep them. They're yours now. Your baby's going to be OK.'

———

Al walked past the tents, whistled softly and waited on the edge of the camp ground. In a few minutes, a blonde girl with a pretty face walked up. She sat down beside Al.

'We're going away tomorrow,' Al said.

'Tomorrow? Where?'

'Up north.'

'But we're going to get married, aren't we?' asked the girl.

'Well, soon.'

'Soon! But you promised,' said the girl. 'And now you're going away. It ain't fair.'

The girl started to get up, but Al caught her and held her arm down, one hand over her mouth. In a moment they were laughing happily together. She was lying on her back – Al bent over her.

'How long do you think you'll be away?' she asked.

'Oh, about a month.'

———

It was still dark when Ma woke the family in the morning.

Ma said, 'Come on, wake up. We've got to be on our way.

85

We've got no coffee. I got a few biscuits. We can eat them on the road. Get up now, and we can load the truck.'

The family dressed. The men loaded up the truck and put the mattresses on top.

'All right, Ma,' said Tom. 'She's ready.'

The truck crawled slowly out of the camp and on to the road. Tom drove until he came to Highway 99 and then turned north towards Bakersfield. Tom drove to the edge of the city and along the great highway.

'Mornings are getting cold,' Tom said. 'Winter's on the way. Hope we can get some money before it comes.'

'Tom,' Ma said, 'we've got to have a house in the winter. We've got to. I hear it rains hard round here. We've got to have a house when the rains come. Winfield ain't strong.'

The sun grew warm and bright. A car stopped on the other side of the road and the man called to Tom.

'You people looking for work?'

Tom stopped the truck.

'We sure are, mister.'

'Can you pick peaches?'

'We can pick anything there is,' Tom said.

'Well, there's plenty of work for you, about forty miles north. Go north to Pixley and turn east. Go about six miles. Ask for the Hooper ranch. You'll find plenty of work there. Get there as soon as you can.'

'Thank you, Mister. We need work awful bad.'

They drove on through the sunny morning fields.

'Might even get some work today,' Tom said.

'With you men working, maybe I'll get credit[7],' said Ma excitedly. 'Then I'll get some coffee, and some flour and meat. And soap. And milk. Got to get some milk for Rosasharn. I wonder where we'll stay.'

In the front seat of the truck, Ma, Tom and Al were very happy.

'I ain't felt so good for a long time,' Ma said. 'We might rent a house for a couple of months. We've got to have a house. And I'm going to store up a lot of food.'

About noon, they reached Pixley. They drove into the little town and turned east along a narrower road.

Then, in front of them, the road was blocked with cars. As they drew near, a policeman held up his hand to stop them.

'Where're you going?'

Al said, 'We're looking for work. Picking peaches.'

'OK.' The policeman moved to the side of the road.

Al saw five cars waiting in front of them.

'That's six now,' called the policeman. 'We can let them through.'

The line of cars moved on. Two police motorcycles went in front and two more followed behind them.

Tom said, 'I don't like this. I wonder what's happening.'

The motorcycle turned off the road and the cars followed. Tom saw a line of men standing in the ditch beside the road. They were yelling and shaking their fists. A high wire gate opened. The six old cars moved through and the gate closed behind them. The motorcycles turned and went back.

Two men with guns stood beside the road. One called, 'Go on, go on. What the hell are you waiting for?'

The cars moved on, turned a bend and there was the Peach Camp.

There were fifty little flat-roofed boxes, each with a door and a window. The group of houses made a square. A water tank stood on the edge of the camp. A little grocery store stood on the other side. At the end of each row of houses stood men with guns, wearing big silver stars on their shirts.

'Want to work?'

'Sure we do.'

'Name?'

'Joad.'

Tom saw a line of men standing in the ditch beside the road.
They were yelling and shaking their fists.

'How many of you?'

'Three men, two women, two kids.'

'Can all of you work?'

'Why – I guess so.'

'OK. Find house sixty-three. Wages five cents a box. Go to work right away.'

A number was painted on the door of each square red house.

'Sixty,' Tom said. 'Must be down here. Sixty-one, sixty-two. There she is.'

Tom parked the truck. The family climbed down and looked about in surprise. Two deputies came up and looked hard at the Joads.

'Name?' one asked.

'Joad,' said Tom. 'I told you. What's happening?'

One of the deputies looked at a long list.

'Joad. That name's not here. Nor the car number. Guess they're OK. Now look here, we don't want no trouble. Do your own work, mind your own business and you'll be all right.'

Tom stared at them.

Ma opened the door of the house and stepped inside. The floor was dirty. There was one room with an old stove and nothing more. Rose of Sharon stood beside Ma.

'We going to live here?'

Ma was silent for a moment.

'Sure,' she said at last. 'It won't be so bad when we wash it out. And it won't let in water when it rains.'

The men unloaded the truck silently. A fear had fallen on them. There was silence everywhere. A woman went by, but she did not look at them. Ruthie and Winfield stayed close to the truck, close to the family.

Tom and Pa were carrying the mattresses into the house when a clerk came up.

'How many of you are going to work?' he asked.

Tom said, 'There's three men. Is the work hard? Can the little fellas help?'

'It's picking peaches. Five cents a box. Anyone can do it.'

Ma stood in the doorway. 'We've got nothing to eat, mister. Do we get paid right away?'

'Well, no, but once you've done some work, you can get credit at the store.'

'Come along, let's hurry,' Tom said. 'Where do we go, mister?'

'I'm going out there now. Come with me.'

Tom, Pa and Al walked down the dirty street and into the orchard. The peaches were little balls of gold and red on the trees. There were piles of empty boxes. The pickers filled their buckets, then put the peaches in the boxes. Then they carried their boxes to the checkers[5].

'Here's three more,' the clerk said to the checkers. 'Pick careful now,' he added to the Joads. 'We don't check no bruised fruit. Here's your buckets. Now get started.'

'Come on, Al,' Tom said.

Tom ran to the trees, worked quickly. One, two, three buckets. The box was full. He picked up the box and hurried to the checkers.

The man looked into the box.

'Can't check that one. Every peach is bruised. You put them in careful or you work for nothing.'

'Why, you . . .' Tom began.

'Now, go easy. I warned you before you started,'

Tom's eyes dropped. 'OK, OK,' he said. He went quickly back to the others.

'Might as well throw your peaches out. They're all bruised. He won't take them. Can't drop them in the bucket. Got to lay them in careful.'

They started again. They handled the fruit gently and the boxes filled more slowly.

'Pick careful now. We don't check no bruised fruit.'

They worked steadily on through the afternoon. After a while, Ruthie and Winfield came up.

'You've got to work,' Pa told them. 'You've got to put the peaches careful into the boxes. One at a time.'

The afternoon passed. Tom carried the full boxes to the checkers.

'That's seven. And that's eight,' Tom said. 'That'll give us forty cents. We can get a nice piece of meat for forty cents.'

In mid-afternoon, Ma came out.

'I would've come before,' she said, 'but Rosasharn fainted.'

Ma looked at the children. 'You've been eating peaches. Well, they'll make you real sick.'

When the sun went down, they had picked twenty boxes.

'Well, that's a dollar. Can we get credit now?' Tom asked the checker.

'Sure, I'll give you a slip for a dollar now.'

Tom took the slip of paper to Ma. 'Here you are,' he said. 'You can get a dollar's worth of stuff at the store.'

Ma said, 'What'll you like to eat?'

'Meat,' said Tom. 'Meat and bread and a big pot of coffee with sugar in.'

———

The company's store was a large shed. Ma opened the door and went in.

A small man with a bald head was standing behind the counter.

'Afternoon,' Ma said. 'I've got a slip here for a dollar.'

'Then you can have a dollar's worth.' the man said. 'Anything you like. A dollar's worth.' The man laughed loudly.

'Thought I'd get a piece of meat.'

'Got all kinds of meat,' the man said. 'Hamburger, that's twenty cents a pound.'

'Looks full of fat to me,' Ma said. 'And I thought hamburger only cost ten cents a pound.'

'Well,' laughed the man, 'maybe it does in town. But if you go to town for it, it'll take about a gallon of gas. Have some bones. Ten cents a pound. Make nice soup.'

Ma sighed. 'Give me two pounds of hamburger.'

'Yes, ma'am. And what else?'

'Well, some bread.'

'Right here. Big loaf, fifteen cents.'

'That there's a twelve cent loaf,' said Ma.

'Sure it is. Go into town and get her for twelve cents. Want potatoes? Five pounds a quarter.'

Ma said angrily, 'I know the price of potatoes. Who owns this here store?'

'Why, the company, ma'am. And they fix the prices.'

Ma looked hard at the man. 'I suppose everyone who comes here gets angry. That's why you laugh. You're ashamed of what you're doing.'

The man didn't answer.

'How much is coffee?' Ma asked him.

'Twenty cents the cheapest, ma'am. And that makes your dollar.'

'Wrap'em² up,' Ma said quickly.

Ma picked up the bags. Then she remembered the sugar.

'We've got no sugar,' she said. 'My boy, Tom, he wants sugar. Look, they're working out there. You give me some sugar and I'll bring the slip in later.'

'I can't do it,' the little man said softly, looking away. 'I'll get into trouble.'

'But we've got more money coming,' said Ma. 'Give me ten cents of sugar.'

'But they'll catch me, ma'am.' He looked at Ma and his face lost its fear. He took ten cents from his pocket.

'There,' he said. He took out a bag and weighed the sugar,

then put a little more in. He put the bag of sugar into Ma's arms.

'Thanks to you,' Ma said quietly. 'I'm learning one thing real good. If you're in trouble, or need help, go to poor people. They're the only ones that'll help, the only ones.'

The door closed behind her and the man looked after her with surprised eyes.

———

The fire roared in the Joad's house. Ma worked quickly while Rose of Sharon sat on a box.

'Feeling better now?' Ma asked. 'You'll have to sit on the bed. I need that box for the fire now.'

The men came in, walking heavily.

'Meat, by God!' said Tom. 'And I smell coffee, too. I'm hungry. Where can we wash, Ma?'

'Go down to the water tank. Take the little fellas with you.'

Ma went back to the stove. She laid out the plates and put two hamburgers on each one. Then a big potato and three slices of bread. The men came in again, their faces and hair dripping with water.

They took the plates and ate silently.

'Got any more, Ma?' Tom asked.

'No,' she said. 'That's all. That's a dollar's worth. They charge extra out here. Tomorrow, you'll work a full day, then we'll have plenty.'

Al wiped his mouth with his sleeve.

'Well, I sure hope so,' he said. 'I'm still hungry.'

He stood up. 'Guess I'll look around,' he said. He walked out into the darkness.

After a while, Tom stood up too.

'I'm going to look around too, Ma,' he said. 'I want to see if those men are still out on the road.'

'Don't get into no trouble, Tom,' Ma said.

'Sure, Ma,' said Tom.

He walked down the street, his hands in his pockets. Down by the gate, two men were sitting. Tom could see the guns in their hands. He turned quietly, and walked back up the road.

16

Tom in Trouble

Tom walked about a hundred yards along the road. He stopped and listened. Then he walked off the road to the right. He moved slowly across a field until he came to the wire fence. Very slowly, he slid under it, holding up the bottom wire with his hands.

A group of men were walking along the edge of the highway. Tom waited until they had gone by and then he followed them.

A stream cut across the highway. There was a small concrete bridge and, low under the bridge, Tom saw a tent. There was a lantern burning inside.

Tom climbed down and found a path. A man was sitting on a box in front of the tent.

'Evening,' Tom said.

'Who are you?'

'Just a fella going by.'

A voice from inside the tent said, 'What's the matter?'

'Casy!' cried Tom. 'Why, Casy, what are you doing here?'

'My God, it's Tom Joad. Come on in, come on in.'

Casy pulled Tom back with him into the tent. Three other men were sitting there.

'This is Tom Joad. He's the fella I told you about,' Casy said. 'Where's your folks, Tom? What are you doing here?'

'We heard there was work here,' said Tom. 'The cops took us to the Peach Camp. I saw a group of fellas outside, shouting. So I came out here to find out what's going on. How the hell did you get here, Casy?'

One of the men said, 'We struck – wouldn't work no more. This is a strike[5].'

'Well, five cents a box ain't much,' Tom said, 'but a fella can eat.'

A heavy silence fell in the tent. Casy stared into the dark night.

'Look, Tom,' he said. 'We came to work here. There was a lot of us. They told us five cents a box. Then when we started, they said they was paying two and a half cents. A fella can't eat for that. So we says we won't work for two and a half cents a box. So the cops came and drove us off. When they've bust[5] this strike, do you think they'll pay you five?'

'Well, they're paying five now,' Tom said.

'Some of us here haven't eaten for days. You go back and tell the others what's happened. You're starving us by working and soon you'll be starving yourselves. As soon as they've driven us out, they'll be giving you two and a half cents. You can't eat for that.'

'I'll try to tell the folks,' Tom said. 'But they don't want to talk. And there are all these guys with guns.'

'Look, Tom,' said Casy. 'Try to get the folks out on strike. Them peaches are ripe. They've got to be picked.'

'They won't strike,' said Tom. 'They're getting five now and they won't listen. Pa won't do it. He'll say it's none of his business.'

'Yes,' said Casy sadly, 'I guess you're right.'

'We had no food,' explained Tom. 'Tonight we had meat. Pa's not going to give up his meat. And Rosasharn needs milk. Ma's not going to starve that baby because of some fellas shouting by a gate.'

One of the men went outside the tent.

'Casy,' he said quietly, 'turn down that lantern and come out here.'

Casy turned down the lantern and went out. Tom followed.

'Listen!'

'I hear,' said Tom. 'There's some fellas coming this way.'

'Let's go,' said Casy. The men moved together under the bridge.

Someone shouted, 'There they are!'

A flashlight shone on the men and blinded them.

'That's him,' said a voice in the darkness.

'Listen,' said Casy. 'You fellas don't know what you're doing. You're helping to starve kids.'

A short, heavy man stepped into the light. He was carrying a new pick-handle.

Casy repeated, 'You don't know what you're doing.'

The heavy man swung the pick-handle. It crashed into the side of Casy's head and he fell.

'Jesus, I think you've killed him!' said one of the men.

The flashlight shone down on Casy's crushed head.

Tom jumped for the pick-handle and grabbed it. Tom's first blow struck the heavy man's head. Tom stood there. There were shouts, the sound of running feet. Something hit Tom hard on the face. He ran along the stream, bending low. He turned and lay still in the bushes. Then he crossed the field again, found the fence and slipped under. His nose was crushed and blood dripped from his chin. He lay down on his stomach till his breath came more easily. Then he bathed his face in the water of the ditch.

The night was quiet again. Tom crossed the ditch and went onto the road. He found the door of the Joad house. The door squeaked.

Ma's voice said, calm and steady, 'What's that?'

The heavy man swung the pick-handle.

'Me, Tom.'

'Well, get some sleep. Al ain't in yet.'

Tom did not sleep. His face throbbed with pain.

Al came back and fell asleep at once.

Dawn came at last and there were sounds of movement in the nearby houses. Ma sat up, found her dress and put it on. She stood by the window for a moment and then woke Pa.

She said, 'Pa, you got more money?'

'Yeah. Got a paper for sixty cents.'

'Well, get up and get some flour and lard for the stove. You fellas have got to eat and start work.'

Pa dressed and went out. Ma's eyes moved towards Tom. She moved quickly to him when she saw his face. It was swollen and blue. His cheek was torn and the blood had dried black on his lips and chin.

'Tom,' she whispered, 'what's the matter?'

'Don't talk loud. I couldn't help it, Ma. I got in a fight. I'm in trouble. I can't work. I've got to hide.'

'Is the trouble bad?'

'Yeah. Bad!'

Pa came back. The others were awake now. They all looked at Tom.

Tom tried to sit up. 'Jesus, I'm weak,' he said. 'I've got to tell you, so I'll tell you all at once.

'Last night, I found Casy. He was leading the strike. Then some fellas came for him. They hit him – killed him. Then I went mad. I took a pick-handle and hit a fella.'

'Did you kill him?' Pa asked.

'I don't know. I tried to.'

'Did they see you?'

'I think so. They had the lights on us.'

For a moment, Ma stared into his eyes. Then she said, 'Pa, we've got to get breakfast. Break up some boxes. You've got to work. Ruthie – Winfield – if anyone asks you, Tom's sick.'

Pa broke the boxes and Ma made the fire.

Pa came near to Tom. 'Casy was a good man. What did he want to strike for?'

Tom told him.

'And now Casy's dead,' said Tom, 'that'll be the end of the strike. We'll get two and a half cents today. You'll see.'

Pa looked out of the window.

'There's a lot of new people coming in,' he said.

'I guess you'll start at two and a half cents,' said Tom.

Ma turned from the stove.

'Listen to me,' she said. 'Tonight we're eating cheap. We're eating cornmeal mush[7]. And as soon as we get enough money for gas, we're moving out. This ain't a good place. Here, eat this and get out to work.'

When the two men had gone off with the children, Ma took a plate and cup to Tom.

'Better eat something.'

'I can't, Ma. My face's too sore. Ma – I didn't know what I was doing. But this fella smashed Casy . . .'

'It's all right,' said Ma. 'I wish you hadn't been there. But you did what you had to do. I can't say you did wrong.'

She went to the stove and dipped a cloth in hot water.

'Here,' she said. 'Put that on your face.'

Tom said, 'I'm going away tonight, Ma. I can't bring trouble on all of you.'

Ma said angrily, 'Tom, you're not going away. The family's breaking up, Tom. Rosasharn's going to have her baby and we need you. Don't go, Tom. Stay and help.'

'OK,' he said. 'I shouldn't stay though, I know it.'

'You sleep here. I'm going to pick now. Rosasharn, if anyone comes, don't let them in. Tom's sick. You hear? Don't let no one in.'

Tom lay still and tried to sleep.

'You – Tom!'

'Yeah?' He looked over at Rosasharn. Her eyes were full of anger.

'You killed a fella! And it ain't the first fella you've killed either.'

'Not so loud! You want to bring someone here?'

'What do I care?' the girl cried. 'What chance have I got to have a nice baby? Connie's gone and I ain't getting good food. I ain't getting milk. And now you kill a fella.'

'Be quiet!'

'You get away from me,' Rosasharn answered. 'I don't want to look at you.' She covered her head with her blanket. Tom could hear her crying.

Tom got up and went to Pa's bed. A rifle lay under the mattress, long and heavy. He took the rifle back to his own mattress and laid it on the floor beside him. He lay down and covered himself with his blanket.

Outside, cars went by and there were voices.

'You go to house twenty-five.'

'OK, mister. What're you paying?'

'Two and a half cents.'

'Why, a man can't eat for that!'

'Either take it, or move on. I didn't fix the price and I've got no time to argue.'

'Number twenty-five, did you say?'

'Yes. Twenty-five.'

17

The Family Secret

In the early evening, Ma came back to the house. She knocked on the door.

'It's me,' she said. 'Did anyone come when I was gone?'

'No,' Tom said. 'How was picking today? I heard they dropped the price.'

Ma said, 'Didn't hardly make nothing. Don't want to talk about it.'

It grew darker. Ma lit the lantern. She poured cornmeal into some hot water.

'Rosasharn, you come now and stir the mush.'

Outside was the noise of running feet. The door burst open and Ruthie rushed in.

'Ma, Winfield's real sick. Got white and fell down. Been eating peaches all day!'

Ma ran heavily up the street with the little girl. A man walked towards her, carrying Winfield. Ma ran up to him.

'He's mine. Give him to me,' she said. She took the little boy, and then she said, 'Thank you,' to the man.

Ma hurried back and laid Winfield on a mattress.

Tom said, 'He's hungry. Got no strength. Get him a can of milk and make him drink it.'

Pa and Al came into the house, carrying bits of stick for the fire.

Ma said, 'How much did we make today?'

'Dollar forty-five.'

'Well, you go right over and get a can of milk for Winfield. He's sick.'

Al said, 'Is mush all we get after working all day? A fella needs meat if he's going to work.'

'You sit quiet,' Ma said. 'There's other things more important. Al, we've got enough gas to go away, haven't we?'

'About a quarter tank,' Al said.

'Right. Then we'll talk after we've had the mush.'

Pa came back with a can of milk. Ma took the can and opened it. She filled a cup and handed it to Tom.

'Give that to Winfield.'

'I can't drink it,' the boy said. 'I'll sick it up.'

'Then don't none of you touch that milk. That's for Winfield, later.'

'I ain't had no milk,' Rose of Sharon said. 'I ought to have some.'

'I know,' said Ma, 'but you're not sick yet. The little fella is. Now, let's eat. You can have sugar in your coffee or on your mush – not both.'

Winfield sat up and drank his milk. Then he took some mush. Ma gave the rest of the milk to Rose of Sharon. She poured coffee in the cups.

'Now, Pa,' Ma said. 'You say what happened today. And you, Ruthie and Winfield, you ain't ever to tell anybody what you hear. That'll break up the family.'

'Well,' Pa said, 'they dropped the price like you said, Tom. The new pickers were so hungry, they'd pick for half a loaf of bread. I said to the checker, "We can't work for two and a half cents a box," and he said, "Well, these fellas can." I said, "They won't when they get fed up." And he said, "We're not worried. We'll have all the peaches picked by then."'

Tom said, 'What about the other thing – that fella that got hit?'

Pa was silent for a while. 'Tom,' he said at last, 'looks like you're in real trouble. People ain't talking about much else. They've got men out looking for the fella.'

Tom said, 'Well, this fella only did it after they killed Casy.'

Pa said, 'That's not what they're saying. They're saying the fella did it first.'

'They know what the fella looks like?' Tom asked.

'Well, not exactly, but they think he'll have a . . .'

Tom put his hand up slowly to his bruised face.

'Ma,' he said, 'perhaps this fella ought to go away.'

Ruthie broke in, 'Ma, me and Winfield knows Tom did it. We know Tom's the fella you're talking about.'

Tom smiled. 'Well, that fella don't want to bring trouble on his folks. Ma, I've got to go.'

Ma got to her feet. 'You ain't going – we're taking you with us. Al, you bring the truck back against the door. We'll put one mattress on the bottom. Tom gets on that. Then we put the others on top, so he can hide. We'll make a fold in the mattress, so he can breathe. Don't argue, that's what we'll do.'

Al backed up the truck. They arranged the mattresses with Tom inside. Everything else went on top. A guard came up, carrying a gun.

'What's going on here?' he asked.

'We're going out,' Pa said. 'We've had a good job offered us, near Weedpatch.'

'Let's have a look at you.' The man flashed his light. 'Wasn't there another fella with you?'

Al said quickly, 'You mean that hitch-hiker[7]? Short fella with a pale face? He went off this morning when the rate dropped.'

'Was his face bruised this morning?'

'I didn't see nothing,' said Al. 'Get in everyone, we've got to get started.'

The guard watched them drive along the street and turn left.

At the gate a guard came to the side of the truck.

'Leaving?'

'Yeah,' said Al. 'Going north. Got a job.'

The guard swung the gate open and the truck turned left and moved towards 101, the great north-south highway.

Tom lifted up one side of a mattress. 'Which way are we

going?' he asked. 'Maybe we ought to keep to side roads.'

Ma said, 'Knock on the back. Get Al to stop.'

The truck pulled to a stop. Al got out and walked to the back. 'What do you want?' he asked.

Ma said, 'Tom says we'd better stay on the side roads.'

'It's my face,' Tom added. 'Any cop would know me. Maybe go north. We've been south.'

'OK,' said Al.

Ma leant back against the side of the truck. 'Gives you a strange feeling, being hunted. I'm getting mean[7].'

'Everybody's getting mean,' Pa said. 'A fellow changes. Down at that government camp we wasn't mean.'

Al turned right. The fruit trees were gone now, and the fields were full of cotton plants. They drove for twenty miles through the cotton, along the country roads.

The road went over a concrete bridge, and followed a stream on the other side. On the edge of the stream, the lights showed a long line of red boxcars[7], without wheels.

A big sign on the edge of the road said: "COTTON PICKERS WANTED". Al slowed down. Tom looked out from under the mattresses. A quarter of mile further on, Tom knocked on the truck again.

'Now what do you want?' Al asked.

'Shut off the engine and climb up here,' said Tom.

Tom crawled out from under the mattresses and knelt in front of Ma.

'Look,' he said. 'They want cotton pickers. When my face gets better, I'll be all right, but not now. You saw those boxcars back there. Now maybe there's work there. How about if you get work and live in one of them cars?'

'How about you?' Ma asked.

'Well, you saw those bushes near the stream. I could hide in there. I saw a good place. And at night, you could bring me something to eat.'

105

The lights showed a long line of red boxcars, without wheels.

Pa said, 'By God, I'd like to get my hands on some cotton. That's work I understand.'

'Them boxcars might be a good place to stay,' said Ma. 'Nice and dry. Do you think there's a place where you could hide, Tom?'

'Sure. As soon as my face gets well, then I'll come out.'

'If we all pick cotton, we could get some money,' Pa said.

'What do we do right now?' Al asked.

'Go back to them boxcars, and sleep in the truck till morning,' Pa said. 'Then we'll get work.'

'How about Tom?' Ma asked.

'You forget me, Ma. I'll take a blanket. And you bring me a little food when it's dark.'

'Take care,' said Ma. 'Take care.'

'Sure I will,' said Tom. He climbed down with his blanket.

'Goodnight,' he said. Ma watched him disappear into the bushes.

Al asked, 'Do I go back now?'

'Yeah,' said Pa.

'Go slow,' said Ma. 'I want to see that place where Tom's going to hide.'

Al turned the truck and drove back to the line of boxcars. The doors were dark. No one moved.

'You climb up the back,' Al said to Rose of Sharon. 'I'll sleep in front here.'

The family lay close together in the back of the truck. The sound of moving water came from the stream.

18

Cotton Picking

The two rows of boxcars stood on a piece of flat land beside the stream. Each boxcar took two families. There were no windows, but the wide doors stood open.

The Joads had one end of a car. Ma hung a curtain across the middle of the car.

'It's nice,' she said. 'It's dry. The rain won't get in here.'

Each night, Ma unrolled the mattresses for the family. Each morning, she rolled them up again. Every day the family went into the field and picked cotton, and every night, they had meat.

On the first Saturday, they drove into Tulare and they bought a tin stove, new overalls for the men and a new dress for Ma. Ma gave her best dress to Rose of Sharon.

'She's so big,' Ma said, 'It's a waste of good money to get her a new dress now.'

The Joads had been lucky. They had arrived early enough to get into a boxcar. The latecomers put up tents near the stream.

The Joads knew how to pick cotton. They quickly filled up the bags and took them to be checked.

Every evening, they walked back from the fields and Ma bought meat at the company store.

'Three pounds of meat,' Ma said, 'and a bottle of milk for my girl.'

The Joads climbed up into their end of the boxcar. Rose of Sharon had started the fire in the tin stove.

'Did you get milk?' she demanded. 'Give it to me. I haven't had any since this morning.'

'You got the potatoes ready?' asked Ma.

'Right here.'

'We'll fry them with the meat,' Ma said.

The men went out to wash in the stream. Rose of Sharon put the potatoes into the frying-pan. The two women were busy over the stove.

Winfield crept in through the door.

'Ma . . .'

'What?'

'Ma – Ruthie told. Told about Tom.'

Ma stared. 'Told?' She knelt in front of him.

'Winfield, tell me. What did she say?'

'Well, some kids were fighting and Ruthie got mad and hit one. Then a big girl hit her. Ruthie said she'd bring her big brother who'd killed two men. When the girl called Ruthie a liar[7], Ruthie said, "Our brother's hiding now from killing a fella". Then she said Tom'd come out now and kill that girl's family too . . .'

'Oh, my sweet Jesus,' said Ma. 'What are we going to do now?' She held her hand to her head. Then she said, 'Winfield, go out and find Ruthie and bring her here.'

As the little boy ran out, Pa came in.

Ma said softly, 'Pa, I've got to tell you. Ruthie's told about Tom and what he's done . . . She got in a fight. Didn't know what she was doing. Now I want you to stay here, Pa. Listen if anyone says anything. I'll take Tom some dinner. I'll tell him to be careful.'

At that moment, Ruthie came in, with Winfield behind her. The little girl's face was dirty and blood dripped from her nose. When Ruthie saw the sad look on Ma's face, she threw herself in Ma's arms and began to shake with sobs.

'Hush[7],' Ma said. 'You didn't know what you were doing. Here. Let go of me. I've got to go now.'

Ruthie went to a corner of the car. Ma put a sheet of newspaper over a plate of food.

'You get on and eat your supper,' she said to Pa. 'I'll have mine when I come back.'

Ma moved quietly down the row of tents. Then she stopped

and looked back. Nobody was watching. Ma walked quietly into the trees.

She walked on until she could see the entrance to the cave where Tom was hiding. A black cloud passed over the sky and a few drops of rain fell. Ma shivered as a cold wind passed through the trees.

Ma heard the sound of a quiet step. A dark shape crept into the open. She called softly, 'Tom, oh, Tom.'

'That you, Ma?'

'Right here. I've got to see you, Tom. Got to talk to you.'

'In here, then. You've got to crawl in . . . Where are you, Ma?'

'Right beside you, Tom. Here, eat this.'

Ma heard him unwrap the food and start eating.

'Meat,' said Tom, 'and fried potatoes. Warm, too.'

Ma said, 'Tom, Ruthie got in a fight and told about you. About you hiding 'cause you'd killed two men. Tom, you've got to go away. Folks'll get talking. How's your face?'

'Getting well quick.'

'Come close, Tom, and let me feel it. You've got a bad scar, Tom. And your nose is all crooked.'

'Maybe that's a good thing. No one'll know me.'

'You've got to go away, Tom.'

'Yeah, I know.'

'Here, Tom, here's seven dollars. Maybe you can take a bus and get far away.'

'I ain't going to take money.'

'Tom,' Ma said. 'You take this money. You've got to. Go to a big city somewhere. They won't look for you there.'

Tom said softly, 'Ma, while I've been sitting here alone, I've been doing a lot of thinking. I've been thinking of Casy. He said a lot of things. He once told me a fella's no good by himself. We've all got to work together. I feel that too, Ma.'

'Casy was a good fella,' Ma said. 'But what are you going to do, Tom?'

'I'm going to do what Casy done. I'm going to get our folks to work together and take care of themselves. All work together – till we can farm our own land again.'

'Tom, they'll hunt you down, like they did Casy.'

'They're going to hunt me down anyway. They're hunting all our people.'

Ma said in the darkness, 'How am I going to know about you, Tom? They might kill you. How am I going to know?'

Tom laughed.

'Well, maybe they can't kill me. I'll still be there when hungry people fight to eat. And I'll be there when our folks are working their own land again. Living in their own houses. See? I'm talking like Casy now. You do a lot of thinking when you ain't moving around. You get back now, Ma.'

'You take the money, then. And Tom, you'll come back, later on? You'll find us?'

'Sure. Now you'd better go. Here, give me your hand. Goodbye now.'

Tom led Ma to the entrance of the cave.

'Goodbye,' she said and she walked quietly away. Her eyes were wet and burning, but she did not cry.

As she went on, the rain began to fall, a few big drops. Ma climbed out on to the road and behind her she heard footsteps. Looking back, she saw a light. In a moment, a man had caught up with her.

'Evening,' he said. 'Looks like we may have a little rain.'

'I hope not. It'll stop the picking. We need the picking.'

'I need the picking too,' said the man. 'I got twenty acres of cotton. I'm looking for pickers now.'

'There's five of us,' said Ma. 'There's not much picking left where we are.'

'I'll put out a sign. Two miles along this road. I'm going down to the camp now.'

'We'll be there in the morning. I hope it don't rain.'

They came to the camp. 'We'll be there,' Ma said.

She went to the boxcar and climbed up inside.

'We got picking tomorrow,' Ma said to Pa. 'Evening, Mr Wainwright,' she added to the man with Pa.

The Wainwrights lived in the same boxcar, on the other side of the curtain.

'Do you suppose we can pick there too?' Wainwright asked.

'Why, sure,' Ma said. 'The fella I met is looking for pickers. You folks can maybe ride in the truck with us.'

Pa said, 'Mr Wainwright's got a worry. That's why he's in our end of the car.'

'What's the matter?'

Wainwright looked down at the floor.

'Our daughter, Aggie,' he said. 'She's a big girl, near sixteen, and grown up. Her and your boy, Al, they're walking out every night. Suppose she got in trouble[7]?'

Ma unrolled a mattress and sat down.

'Well, Al's a good boy,' she said. 'I couldn't ask for a better boy.'

'Oh, we like Al. But what if you go away, or we go away, and we find our Aggie's in trouble. We don't want no shame in our family.'

Ma said softly, 'We'll see you don't have no shame because of us. Pa will talk to Al. Or if Pa won't, I will.'

Wainwright said, 'Goodnight then, and we sure thank you.' He went round the end of the curtain and they could hear him talking quietly to his wife.

'I found Tom,' Ma said softly. 'I . . . I sent him away. Far off. He's a good boy.' And then she added, 'I'm sorry. I shouldn't have said I'll talk to Al. It's your business.'

'I know,' Pa said. 'But I ain't no good any more. Spend all my time thinking how things used to be. It's strange, women taking over[7] the family. I don't even care.'

'A woman can change better than a man,' Ma said. 'Don't you

worry. Maybe next year we can get our own place.'

'We got nothing now,' Pa said. 'Soon there'll be no work. No work in California in the winter. And Rosasharn's baby's coming soon. It seems like our life is over and done.'

'No it ain't,' Ma smiled. 'It ain't, Pa. That's one thing a woman knows. We ain't going to die out.'

There were quiet footsteps outside and Al came in.

'Al,' Ma said, 'we've been talking. Come and sit here.'

'Sure, I want to talk too. I'll have to be going away soon. Me and Aggie Wainwright – we plan to get married. I'm going to get a job in a garage and we'll rent a house. That's what we'll do. And nobody can stop us.'

They stared at him.

'Al,' Ma said, 'We're glad. You're a grown man. You need a wife. But just stay till spring. Who'd drive the truck?'

Mrs Wainwright looked round the curtain.

'Have you heard?' she said. 'They're going to get married. I wish we had a cake.'

'I'll put on coffee, and make some pancakes,' said Ma, standing up.

'And I've got sugar.' Mrs Wainwright said. 'We'll put sugar in those pancakes.'

Ma lit the stove. Ruthie and Winfield sat up in the corner where they had been sleeping.

Ma was making the pancakes when Rose of Sharon climbed up into the boxcar.

'What's happening?' she asked.

'We've had news while you've been out,' Ma cried. 'We're going to have a party – Al and Aggie Wainwright are going to get married!'

Rose of Sharon stood still and looked at Al. Mrs Wainright shouted, 'Aggie's putting a new dress on. We'll be with you in a minute.'

Rose of Sharon turned slowly. She went to the door and

Ma lit the stove.

walked out of the boxcar.

She moved slowly towards the stream and into the trees. The wind was blowing now. Rose of Sharon went down on her knees and crawled into the bushes. When she felt the bushes all round her, she stopped. She stretched out on her back. And she felt the weight of the baby inside her.

19

The Rains

Ma woke, pushed back the blanket and got up. She walked to the door and stood looking out. There was a little light in the east. The wind was blowing and there was frost in the air. Ma shivered. Then she turned back and lit the lantern. She broke sticks and soon the fire was burning.

Rose of Sharon sat up. 'I'm going out to pick cotton,' she said.

'You don't need to.'

'I'm going.'

'All right,' Ma said, 'but don't work too hard. You're near your time⁷.'

Ma put meat in the pan and slowly the family came to life.

'Get out and wash,' Ma told them.

Al said, 'What've we got to get up so early for? We can't pick cotton in the dark, Ma.'

'It's only twenty acres,' Ma said. 'Got to be there before it's all picked. Al, soon as you're ready, get the truck started. You nearly ready, Mrs Wainwright?' she called.

'Just eating. Be ready in a minute.'

Ma looked hard at Rose of Sharon. 'Take a blanket,' she said, 'then if you rest, you can keep warm.'

The truck roared. Wainwrights and Joads climbed in.

'We're going to be first there,' Ma said. They drove along the dark road. When they came to the sign: "COTTON PICKERS WANTED", the yard was already full of cars.

'We ain't as early as we thought,' said Al.

The owner took names, wrote them in his book.

'All right, go out when you want,' he said. 'It's light enough to see.'

The cars were still moving in from the highway.

The line of people moved out across the field. The strong wind blew their clothes.

Pa looked quickly at the western hills. Big grey clouds were moving over them.

'They look like rain-clouds,' he said. And all down the cotton rows, the people looked back at the clouds. They bent lower and picked faster. They raced against the rain and against each other. And now the high grey clouds moved over the sky towards the rising sun.

At eleven o'clock, the field was picked and the work was done. The pickers stood in line to get their money. The families went back to their cars silently. And they drove slowly away.

As the Joads and Wainwrights got into the truck, the first drops of rain began to fall. Ma sat in the front with Rose of Sharon.

'You shouldn't have come,' Ma said. Rose of Sharon shivered suddenly, but she did not reply.

'Go faster, Al,' Ma cried. 'Rosasharn's shivering. She's got a cold. We've got to get her feet in hot water.'

Al drove the truck right up to the boxcar.

'You men, go and get wood,' Ma said. 'We've got to keep warm.'

Rose of Sharon tried to walk, but her knees bent. Mrs Wainwright saw her.

'Has her time come?' she asked Ma.

116

'No, I don't think so,' said Ma. 'Maybe she's got a cold. Help me, will you?'

The older woman helped Rose of Sharon up into the boxcar.

'I'll get a fire going,' Mrs Wainwright said. The rain was pouring down now, beating on the roof of the car.

Ma said, 'Thank God we've got a good roof. Tents always leak.'

'Cover me up, Ma. I'm cold,' Rose of Sharon said. Ma piled all the blankets on top of her. The men returned, their arms piled high with sticks.

'Jesus, it's wet out there,' Pa said.

Ma said, 'Better go back and get more wood. It'll be dark pretty soon. Ruthie and Winfield, you stay here.'

The rain fell, hour after hour. The men brought wood and piled it near the door. Their clothes ran with water.

'All right, now, get off those clothes,' Ma said. 'I've got some nice coffee for you fellas. And you put on dry clothes.'

The evening came early. In the boxcars, the families sat together, listening to the pouring rain on the roofs.

———

On the second day of the rains, Al took down the cover curtain from the middle of the car. He spread it over the engine of the truck. Now the two families were one.

All over the camp, the water stood in puddles and the rain splashed in the mud. The little stream rose up nearer to the flat ground where the boxcars stood.

On the third day, the Wainwrights grew worried.

'Maybe we'd better move on,' Mrs Wainwright said.

Ma tried to keep them there. She watched Al.

Rose of Sharon had a fever and a heavy cold. Ma tried to make her drink hot milk. Rose of Sharon shook her head weakly.

'I ain't hungry,' she said.

The men watched the water rising in the stream.

Pa said, 'If it comes up any higher, it'll flood us. But if we all dug and made the bank higher, I guess we'd be OK.'

Wainwright said, 'I think we should get out of here.'

Al said, 'Pa, if they go, I'm going too. Me and Aggie've got to stay together.'

Pa looked surprised. 'You can't go, Al. The truck . . . We ain't going to find another nice place like this. Come on, now. Let's talk to the other fellas.' They went along to the next car.

Ma was at the stove, keeping the fire burning with a few sticks.

'I'm hungry,' Ruthie said. 'There ain't nothing to do. Ain't no fun.'

'There'll be fun,' Ma said. 'You wait. But don't bother me now, Ruthie. Rosasharn's sick.'

Rose of Sharon gave a quick, sharp cry. She held her breath and her face was full of fear.

Ma called, 'Oh, Mrs Wainwright! Look!' Ma pointed at Rose of Sharon's face.

'I think her time's come,' Ma said. 'It's early. Maybe the fever started it.'

'She's got to get to her feet, walk around,' Mrs Wainwright said. 'Come on, let's close that door. I'll get our lamp. Ruthie, you and Winfield go down the end of the car with Aggie.'

'I want to watch, Ma. I want to watch Rosasharn have her baby.'

'Ruthie, you get away now. Get away quick.'

Ruthie and Winfield stood behind the pile of wood.

'Don't you make no noise,' Ruthie said to Winfield. 'When Ma's busy, we can watch.'

'You're going to have a nice baby,' Ma said to Rose of Sharon. 'Get up and walk now. Try. We'll help you.' Then Ma held her on one side and Mrs Wainwright on the other.

Rose of Sharon went stiff and gave a cry of pain. They laid her on the mattress until the pain passed. Then they helped her up again and began to walk.

Pa put his head through the small opening. 'What did you shut the door for?' he asked.

Ma said, 'Her time's come.'

'Then we couldn't leave here if we wanted to. We've got to build that bank.'

'That's right. You've got to.'

Pa walked through the mud to the stream. Twenty men stood there in the rain. Pa cried, 'We've got to build that bank. My girl's got her pains. We can't go now.'

A tall man said, 'It ain't our baby. We can go.'

'Sure,' Pa said. 'You can go. Nobody's stopping you.'

He hurried to the lowest part of the bank and drove the shovel into the mud. The other men began to work beside him. The men worked furiously. When one man dropped his shovel, another took it up.

A scream came from the Joad car. The men stopped, listened for a moment and then went back to work again.

The water in the stream moved slowly up the side of the new bank.

'Higher!' Pa cried. 'We've got to get her higher!'

The evening came and the work went on. The men were tired, but they worked on, like machines. When it was dark, the women put lanterns in the car doors.

Rose of Sharon's pains were coming closer now. She screamed and screamed. Women came in, looked at the girl kindly, and went back to their own cars. For a long time, the screams continued and then, at last there was silence. The rain fell steadily.

Pa said, 'Ma'd tell me if the baby was born,' and he went on digging out the mud. There was a crash. Higher up the stream, a great tree had fallen. The tree fell into the water and moved slowly down the stream. The men watched as the branches turned

The men worked furiously.

and tore at the new bank. The water piled up behind the tree and then began to pour through the bank. The men turned and ran. The water moved slowly on to the flat ground. It moved under the boxcars, under the trucks.

Al ran quickly to the truck. He pulled off the cover and tried to start the engine. He tried again and again, but the motor was full of water. Other cars were started, but their wheels sank deeper and deeper into the mud.

Pa climbed up through the narrow opening into the boxcar.

'How is she?' Pa asked. Ma looked up once, quickly, and then down again.

'All right I think. Sleeping now.'

Mrs Wainwright led Pa to a box in the corner of the car. She held the lantern over the box.

'The baby never breathed, it never was alive,' she said.

Pa walked slowly over to Ma. She looked at Pa for a moment, her eyes wide and staring.

Pa said, 'We done what we could. We worked all night. But the water's come under the car now.'

'I know, I heard it,' said Ma.

'Don't know how high the water will rise. It might flood the car.'

'I know.'

'Is Rosasharn going to be all right? Is there anything different we could have done?' Pa asked.

'No, there was only one thing to do, and we did it.' Ma looked at Pa with a smile of pity and love on her white lips.

From outside, there came the sound of an angry voice.

'Where's that fool, Joad. If he hadn't had that fool idea about the bank, we'd have got out.'

Al's voice answered, 'If you go in, you fight me first!'

Pa got slowly to his feet and went to the door.

'All right, Al, I'm coming out. We've got sickness in here,' he said to the angry men.

'Why don't you get some sleep?' Mrs Wainwright said to Ma. 'I'll sit with her.'

Ma smiled. 'You've been friendly.' she said. 'We thank you.'

'No need to thank. If we were in trouble, you'd help us.'

'Yes,' said Ma, 'we would. At one time all we cared for was the family. Now we care for anybody. The worse things get, the more we've got to do for each other.'

And Ma stretched out on the mattress beside the sleeping girl. Mrs Wainwright sat on the floor and kept watch.

20

In the Barn

Pa and Al sat in the doorway and watched the dawn come. The rain had stopped, but the sky was heavy with clouds. As the light came, they saw that the flood water was still rising.

'Do you think it'll come inside the car?' Al asked.

Pa said, 'I don't know. Might start to rain again.'

Al said, 'I've been thinking. I reckon the water'll come up into the car, about three or four feet.'

'Yeah.'

'We can't get away from here. We could take the boards from the side of the truck and build a kind of platform inside the boxcar. We could take everything up into the platform with us. That way, we'll keep everything dry.'

'The water's getting higher,' Pa said, 'I guess we'd better do that.'

Ma turned restlessly in her sleep. She cried, 'Tom, oh, Tom!'

Mrs Wainwright got up and pointed to the box where the dead baby lay, covered with a piece of cloth.

'That's causing trouble and sorrow here. Couldn't you fellas bury it?'

'Guess you're right,' Pa said. 'It's against the law, but I'll do it.'

He took a shovel and Mrs Wainwright gave him the box.

Al started to work on the truck. When Pa came back, he helped Al carry the planks into the boxcar. Ma sat up.

'What're you doing?' she said.

'Going to build a platform in here. That way, we'll keep out of the wet. The water's coming up all the time.'

'We've got to get out of here,' Ma said.

'We can't,' said Al. 'The truck's here, everything we've got.'

Ma looked at Pa. 'You'd better get down to the store. We need stuff for breakfast.' She went back to the mattress and looked at Rose of Sharon.

'How do you feel?' Ma asked her.

'Tired, real tired, Ma . . .?'

'Yeah? What do you want, Rosasharn?'

'Is . . . is the baby all right?'

Ma knelt down on the mattress. 'You can have more,' she said. 'We did everything we could.'

The girl lay back and covered her eyes with her arms.

Pa came in with the food. Ma built up the fire with the last of the sticks.

'We got any money left now?' Ma asked him.

'No,' said Pa.

Ma sighed. 'Now what are we going to do?

As they ate, the water crept up and up. Al and Pa ate quickly. They built the platform: five feet wide, six feet long, four feet above the floor. The water was moving across the floor now. And outside, the rain began again.

Al said, 'Come on, now, let's get the mattresses and blankets up.'

They lifted Rose of Sharon, on her mattress, on top of the pile.

123

At the other end of the car, the Wainwrights built a platform for themselves.

Ma looked down. There was half an inch of water on the floor now. She said suddenly, 'We've got to get out.'

'We can't,' Pa said. 'All our stuff's here.'

———

During the day and night, the water rose to six inches deep on the floor of the car. On the morning of the second day, Pa splashed through the camp and came back with ten potatoes in his pocket. Ma watched him break up part of the car wall to make a fire. The family ate the hot boiled potatoes with their fingers. When the last food had gone, they stared down at the grey water. They did not sleep for a long time.

In the morning, Ma said, 'We're getting out of here. We're getting to higher ground. You men can come or not, but I'm taking Rosasharn and the little fellas out of here.'

'We can't,' said Pa weakly.

'All right then. But you'll get Rosasharn to the highway and then come back.'

Al said, 'Ma, I ain't going – Aggie and me . . .'

Ma smiled. 'Of course. You stay here and look after the stuff, Al. When the water goes down, we'll come back. Come on, Rosasharn, Pa'll carry you to the road.'

Pa stood in the water, waiting. Ma helped Rose of Sharon down from the platform and Pa carried her through the deep water to the highway. He put her on her feet and came back for Ruthie. Ma stood in the water.

'Winfield, sit on my shoulder,' Ma said. 'Al, if Tom comes, tell him we'll be back. Tell him to be careful.' She walked off through the water.

They stood on the highway and looked back at the truck and

the boxcars and the slowly moving water. As they stood, a little rain began to fall.

'We got to get along,' Ma said. 'Rosasharn, you try to walk now.'

Pa complained, 'Now, where're we going? Where're we going?'

'I don't know. Come on, help Rosasharn. We're going some place where it's dry.'

They went slowly along the road. The sky grew darker and the rain was heavier.

'We've got to hurry,' Ma said. 'If this girl gets wet, I don't know what'll happen to her.'

Far off the road, on a small hill, stood a barn.

'Look,' Ma said. 'We'll go there. I bet it's dry in that barn. Hurry up. There's more rain coming.'

The storm broke. Heavy rain fell on them. They struggled through mud up the little hill. Rose of Sharon's feet slipped. Pa stopped a minute and picked her up. They reached the open end of the barn. The rain fell heavily on the roof. Pa gently put Rose of Sharon down on an old box.

Ma said, 'Maybe there's hay inside. Look, there's a door.' She swung it open. 'There is hay!' she cried. 'Bring her in here, Pa. Come on you little fellas.'

Winfield said, 'Ma! Look! in the corner.'

Ma looked. There were two people: a man on his back and a boy sitting beside him. The boy got slowly to his feet.

'Do you own this place?' he asked.

'No,' said Ma. 'We've come in out of the wet. We've got a sick girl. You got a dry blanket we could use?'

The boy went back to the corner and brought a dirty blanket.

'Thank you,' Ma said. 'What's the matter with that fella?'

The boy said, 'He's sick. He's starving. Hasn't eaten for six days.'

Ma walked to the corner and looked down at the man.

They stood on the highway and looked back at the truck and the boxcars and the slowly moving water.

'Your Pa?' she asked.

'Yeah. He gave me all the food. Now he's weak. He can't move.'

'He'll be all right,' Ma said. 'You wait until I get the wet clothes off my girl.'

Ma held up the blanket while Rose of Sharon took off her clothes. Then Ma wrapped the blanket round her.

Suddenly the boy said, 'My Pa's dying. He's starving to death. He's got to have some milk . . .'

'Hush,' said Ma. She looked at Rose of Sharon. The two women looked into each other's eyes. The girl breathed quickly.

'Yes,' she said.

Ma smiled. 'I knew you would, I knew.'

Rose of Sharon whispered, 'Will . . . will you all go out?'

Ma got up quickly. 'Come on, you fellas,' she called. 'You come out with me.' She bent down and kissed Rose of Sharon on the forehead. She moved the others quickly through the door and shut it behind her.

For a minute, Rose of Sharon sat still. Then she moved slowly to the corner. She looked down into the man's wide, frightened eyes. Then slowly she lay down beside him. He shook his head slowly from side to side.

'You've got to have milk,' she said. She pulled his head close. Rose of Sharon loosened the blanket and uncovered her breast.

'There,' she said. 'There.' Her hand held his head gently.

She looked across the barn and smiled.

Points for Understanding

1

1 Everywhere there was dust. What was the dust doing to the corn?
2 The men were getting ready to fight back. What were they going to fight against?
3 Which state did the Joad family live in?
4 What had happened to the Joad farm?
5 Why had Tom Joad been sent to jail?
6 How long had he been in jail?
7 'Your Grampa stood out here with a rifle.'
   (a) Whose Grampa is this?
   (b) Where is 'here'?
   (c) Why had Grampa held a rifle?

2

1 Who did the owner men say owned the land?
2 Who did the tenant farmers say owned the land and why?
3 What did the owner men want to plant on the land?
4 'You small farmers must go.' What was going to come instead of the small farmers?
5 'There's work there and it never gets cold.' Where was this?

3

1 What did Tom see in the yard when he arrived at the Rances' farm?
2 A look of fear came into his eyes. Why was Tom's father afraid when he saw his son again?
3 What was Tom's Ma doing?
4 Tom had two brothers and two sisters. What were their names and ages?
5 What two things did Tom now know about the older of his two sisters?
6 Who were the little fellas?
7 How many miles was the journey to California?

4

1 Why did Casy not sit with the others by the truck at first?
2 How much money were the Joads taking with them to California?
3 'I wonder if all of us can ride on the truck, and the preacher too.'
    (a) What was Ma's reply to these words?
    (b) How many people were going on the truck?
4 What did Ma do with the pair of earrings and the gold ring?
5 'This country ain't no good, but it's my country. I'll stay here.'
  Who said these words and did he stay?
6 Who drove the truck when they set off?

5

1 What speed did the truck travel at? Why did Al not drive faster?
2 'Any hills between here and California, Ma?' What was Ma's reply?
3 What was the name of the great road to the west?
4 Steinbeck calls this great road the road of flight. Who were the
  people in flight and what were they fleeing from?
5 Why was Ma worried about Tom crossing the state line?
6 Why was Tom not worried?
7 The Joads stopped for the night near the road. Who did they meet
  there?

6

1 'You're from Kansas . . . you talk different.' When Al said these
  words what did Sairy Wilson reply?
2 Why were the Joads grateful to the Wilsons?
3 Why did the Joads not report Grampa's death?
4 What did they put into the grave with Grampa's body, and why?
5 Why was Rose of Sharon scared?
6 The Wilsons had been on the road for three weeks. Why had they
  taken so long to get this far?
7 Pa showed Wilson a handbill.
    (a) What sort of work did the bill mention?
    (b) Were the wages good?
    (c) How many pickers were wanted?
    (d) Had Wilson seen the bill before?
    (e) Why was Wilson worried?
    (f) Why was Pa not worried?

7

1 What was Connie planning to do when he reached California?
2 'What have we got left in the world?' Who asked the question and what was the answer?
3 Why did Tom and Al go off to town on their own?
4 In the camp ground, the Joads and Wilsons met a man who had been to California.
    (a) How long had the man stayed there?
    (b) What had happened to his family while he was there?
    (c) What did he say about the handbills?
    (d) Why did he say he was going home?
5 Why did Tom, Al, and Casy not sleep in the camp?

8

1 In the river, the men met a stranger and his boy. The stranger told them, 'It's good land, but it ain't yours.' What did he mean?
2 What did the word 'Okie' mean and who used the word?
3 'He wore a gun and there was a big silver star on his shirt.' What was this man's job and what did he tell Ma to do?
4 Why did the Wilsons decide not to cross the desert with the Joads?
5 Why did the Joads not wait for a few more days?

9

1 'First she says Granma's sick, then she says she's all right.' What was Ma's reason for hiding Granma's death?
2 'I wish *they* could have seen *it*.' Who is 'they' and what is 'it'?
3 How much money did the Joads have left?

10

1 Why were the landowners afraid of the Okies?
2 Why did the shopkeepers hate the Okies?
3 The Okies wanted only two things. What were they?
4 What were the landowners afraid that the Okies might find?

11

1 Why was Connie angry and why did he wish he'd stayed at home?
2 Ma heard about a nice camp. What sort of camp was it and where was it?
3 Did a family need money to stay there?
4 What did Floyd Knowles say which angered the contractor?
5 'He's talking red.' The contractor said this about Floyd. What did he mean?
6 Where did the contractor say there was plenty of work?
7 The deputy said, 'This camp's real dirty. We've got to clean it out.' How were the police going to clean out the camp?
8 Casy said to Tom, 'You've got to get out.' What had Tom done and why was Tom in danger?
9 Who took the blame for the trouble at the camp?

12

1 What had happened to Connie?
2 Why did Ma tell Pa not to say bad things about Connie?
3 The light grew brighter. What was the light which the Joads saw?
4 Ma asked Tom, 'Where're we going?' Where was Tom going?

13

1 The government camp at Weedpatch was very different from other migrant camps. What do you think pleased Tom most about it?
2 How was Mr Thomas different from other landowners?
3 What warning did Mr Thomas give to Tom?
4 What sort of work did Al really want to do?
5 Ma said, 'This here's a nice place. We could be happy here.' What was Pa's reply?

14

1 Three men at the dance said they had been invited by a man called Jackson. What was their reason for coming to the dance?
2 Why were the deputy sheriffs turned away from the gate?
3 Were the three troublemakers Californians or migrants?

1 Why did the Joads decide to leave the government camp?
2 Pa said, 'Once the man decided what to do.' Who decided what to do now?
3 What did Ma give Rosasharn before they left the government camp?
4 Ma said, 'We've got to have a house.' What was her main reason for wanting a house?
5 What work did the Joads find at the Hooper ranch?
6 What was the 'rate' for the job?
7 What was happening in the ditch beside the entrance to the ranch?
8 Why were the prices at the store so high?
9 How did the man at the store help Ma?

16

1 Why were Casy and the other men on strike?
2 What did Casy want Tom to tell the pickers at the camp?
3 Ma said to Tom, 'You did what you had to do.' What had Tom done and where did he hide?
4 Tom said, 'I'm going away tonight.' Why did Ma stop him from going?
5 Casy had told Tom, 'As soon as they've driven us out, they'll be giving you two and a half cents.' Was Casy right?

17

1 'You can have sugar in your coffee or on your mush – not both.' Why not?
2 A guard asked, 'Wasn't there another fella with you?' when the Joads left the camp. What was Al's reply? What was the truth?
3 The Joads saw a sign on the edge of the road. What did the sign say?
4 Where did the Joads stop for the night?
5 Why did Tom not sleep in the truck?

18

1 Where did the Joads make their new home and who did they share it with?
2 Ma told Tom, 'You've got to go.' Why had she changed her mind?
3 Ma asked Tom, 'What are you going to do?' What did he reply?
4 What did Ma give to Tom before she left him?
5 Who did Ma meet on the way back to the boxcar and what did he tell her?
6 What did Al plan to do?
7 What did Rose of Sharon do when she had heard Al's news?

19

1 What did Pa persuade the other men to do about the bank of the stream?
2 Ma said, 'Her time's come.' What did she mean by this?
3 Why were the cars unable to leave the camp?
4 Who had helped Ma when Rose of Sharon began her pains?
5 What happened to Rose of Sharon's baby?
6 Ma said, 'At one time all we cared for was the family.' How had her life in California changed this?

20

1 What did Al and Pa do to keep everything dry in the boxcar?
2 Where did Ma and Pa take Rose of Sharon and the children?
3 Who did they meet there?
4 How did Rose of Sharon save a man's life?

Glossary

SECTION 1

American expressions

The language used by the people in this story is the language of the working people of America – the migrants, the small farmers, etc. These people had their own use of words and their own grammar. This section gives examples of the words they used. Section 2 lists examples of the short forms which were common in their speech. And Section 3 lists examples of their grammatical usage.

This kind of American English is commonly used by young people in many parts of the English-speaking world.

fellas (page 19)
>an American way of saying fellows, meaning people, usually men. The 'little fellas' are the Joads' two younger children.

folks (page 13)
>often used to mean a person's family. Sometimes used to mean people in general.

good and welcome (page 32)
>welcome.

guess – *Guess* (page 27)
>I think.

guy (page 45)
>a man.

Hi (page 41)
>Hello

honey (page 66)
>a word used when speaking to someone you love.

kid (page 22)
>child.

long – *so long* (page 10)
>goodbye.

place (page 11)
>the place where a person's home is.

proud to have you (page 32)
>pleased that you've come.

reckon – *I reckon* (page 34)
  I think.
real bad – *sick real bad* (page 33)
  very ill.
red – *talking red* (page 62)
  a red was a communist. Somebody who talked red was thought to
  be a troublemaker.
yeah (page 13)
  yes.

SECTION 2

Short forms

This list gives a number of examples of short forms which are used in
the Direct Speech passages in this story. Many other examples will be
found in the story.

ain't – *I ain't* (page 14)
  I'm not.
'cause (page 61)
  because.
'em – *wrap 'em up* (page 93)
  wrap them up.
gonna – *it's gonna be all right* (page 50)
  it's going to be all right.
would've (page 11)
  would have.

SECTION 3

Unusual grammatical usage

awful – *awful sick* (page 46)
  very sick.
crime – *done a crime* (page 31)
  committed a crime.
good – *done good* (page 68)
  did well.
got – *got sent to jail* (page 13)
  was sent to jail.

mighty – *mighty nice* (page 72)
   very nice.
nothing – *ain't nothing wrong with me* (page 27)
   There isn't anything wrong with me.
   The double negative is a common feature of the farmer's speech
   in this story. Another example on page 27 is 'This country ain't
   no good' (isn't any). You will find many other examples of this
   usage in the Direct Speech passages in this story.
right – *Al's done right* (page 25)
   Al did the correct thing.
was – *we was* (page 78)
   we were.
weren't – *Connie weren't* (page 65)
   Connie wasn't.

SECTION 4

Expressions showing surprise

Gee – *Gee, what a load!* (page 28)
God – *Thank God* (page 21)
Heavens – *Great Heavens!* (page 18)
Hell – *What the hell!* (page 63)
Jesus – *Sweet Jesus this feels good* (page 73)
Why – *Why, it's the Reverend Casy!* (page 13)

SECTION 5

Terms to do with farming and farm work

Association – *Farmer's Association* (page 72)
   the farmers grouped themselves together in an association. The
   association made sure that the prices the farmers got for their
   crops were kept high and the wages paid to the pickers were kept
   low.
Bank – *The Bank owns the land* (page 14)
   many of the landowners were lent money by a bank in order to
   buy their land. They had to pay money to the bank every year to
   pay the interest on these loans. This is why the owners say that it
   is really the bank who owns the land.

barn (page 11)

a building on a farm. Hay and other crops are stored in the barn. Horses and farm machinery were also often kept in the barns.

bust – *bust a strike* (page 96)

to break. See *strike* below.

checker (page 90)

the man who checks the number of boxes of peaches and makes sure the fruit is not damaged is called a checker.

committee (page 70)

the migrant farm workers in the Government Camp made their own rules. They chose a number of people to look after the camp and to see that everybody kept to the rules. These people formed the Committee.

contract (page 61)

the landowners did not arrange the picking of their own crops. They employed other people – *the contractors* – to do this. The contractors had to have permission from the government – *a licence*. These contractors then found workers to pick the crop. And it was the contractors who paid the pickers. The contractors tried to make as much money as possible by paying the pickers very low wages.

contractor (page 62)

see *contract* above.

cotton – *bolls of cotton* (page 10)

the bolls of cotton are pieces of soft fibre which grow on the cotton plant. These pieces of fibre are picked from the cotton plant and then made into thread and cloth.

farmers – *tenant farmers* (page 14)

tenant farmers are small farmers. They do not own the land they plant their crops on. Most of the money these farmers get from their crops has to be given to the landowners to pay the rent. The *tenant system* was the way in which the tenant farmers worked for the landowners.

hire – *licence to hire men* (page 61)

see *contract* above.

loan – *bank loan* (page 72)

see *Bank* above.

rate – *the rate's twenty-five* (page 72)

the rate is the amount of money that will be paid for each hour a man works. Sometimes the rate is not calculated by the time

137

worked, but by the amount of the crop which is picked – for example, five cents was paid for each box of peaches which a worker picked.

strike – *This is a strike* (page 96)

the pickers sometimes fought against the low wages paid to them by refusing to work. The pickers hoped that the crops would start to go bad and then the contractors would be forced to pay them higher wages. The contractors fought against the pickers who went on strike, by bringing in other workers to do the picking. This is how the contractors *bust* the strike.

system – *tenant system* (page 15)

see *farmers* above.

SECTION 6

Terms to do with the law and the police

cop (page 48)

a policeman.

coroner (page 54)

the coroner is the government official responsible for giving the death certificate and for checking that the dead body is buried correctly.

papers (page 19)

a person who had been in prison had to carry a certificate with him – his papers – saying who he was and when he had been set free from prison.

parole (page 13)

if a person in prison behaves well, he can be paroled – set free – before he has finished his jail sentence. When he is on parole, the person must always carry his papers with him (see *papers* above). Also, he must stay in his home state and not cross the boundary from one state to another. He must regularly visit the police station where he is living, so that the police can check he has not broken the law again. When Tom crossed the Oklahoma state boundary, he was doing something for which he could be sent back to prison.

sheriff – *deputy sheriff* (page 41)

in American towns in the west, the man responsible for law and order is called the sheriff. The sheriff can ask other men to help him and these men are called deputy sheriffs or deputies. The deputy sheriffs wear silver stars on their coats to show that they are working for the sheriff. Deputy sheriffs were often local landowners who wanted to keep the migrant workers from settling anywhere in California.

state line – *cross a state line* (page 31)
> see *parole* above.

star – *big silver star* (page 46)
> see *sheriff* above.

warrant (page 70)
> a signed paper that a policeman must carry, with the criminal's name on, before he can arrest him.

years – *I got seven years* (page 13)
> Tom was sentenced to seven years in prison for killing a man.

SECTION 7

General

boxcar (page 105)
> a covered railway wagon. Farm workers lived in old wagons whose wheels had been removed.

credit (page 86)
> if you have credit at a shop, you can buy goods and pay the money later.

dirt – *a dirt road* (page 10)
> a rough road in the country, often going from one farm to another.

easy – *take it easy* (page 68)
> stay calm and don't get excited and angry.

gas (page 29)
> petrol

highway (page 10)
> a main road running between cities.

hitch-hiker (page 104)
> a person travelling from one place to another by asking drivers of cars or lorries to take him with them. When a driver agrees to take a hitch-hiker with him, he gives the person a *lift*.

hood (page 22)
> the bonnet of the car.

hush (page 109)
> stop crying. A word used to comfort someone who is crying.

liar (page 109)

someone who does not tell the truth.

lift (page 10)

see *hitch-hiker* above

mean – *I'm getting mean* (page 105)

I'm becoming hard and tough. A mean person is someone who is selfish and unkind.

migrant – *migrant road* (page 31)

Highway 66 is a main road running across America to the west. When the people of Oklahoma lost their farms and their work they moved towards California in the west. These people were the migrants – moving from one place to another – and they were travelling along Highway 66–the migrant road.

mush – *cornmeal mush* (page 100)

cornmeal mixed with water. This was a cheap and simple food eaten by people who were very poor.

nursery (page 77)

a place where babies and very young children are looked after while their parents are at work.

over – *take over* (page 112)

to take the responsibility for something.

overalls (page 11)

clothing worn by working people. The men in the illustration on page 91 are wearing overalls.

partners (page 81)

a man and a woman dancing together are each other's partners.

parts – *spare parts* (page 25)

when a car engine has been used for some time and is getting old, some of the parts of the engine break or become useless. These *worn out* parts have to be thrown away and new parts put in. These new parts are called *spare parts*.

preacher (page 13)

a man who speaks to people about God and Jesus and about the Bible. Casy had been a preacher, but he was not a priest or a minister of the church. But the people he spoke to called him *Reverend* – a title which is usually only given to a priest or a minister.

Reverend (page 13)

see *preacher* above.

scare – *don't scare her* (page 19)
   don't frighten her – don't make her afraid.
steady – *steady work* (page 45)
   a job which lasts for a long time and brings money to a worker's
   family for month after month.
stroke (page 33)
   a sudden illness which affects the brain.
stuff (page 23)
   many different things together.
sulking (page 33)
   when a person or a child is unhappy and will not speak to
   anyone, they are said to be *sulking*.
time – *near your time* (page 115)
   time here refers to the time when Rose of Sharon will have her
   baby.
trouble (page 112)
   if the Wainwright's daughter, Aggie, has a baby and is not
   married to Al, this will be considered disgraceful and it will bring
   shame to the Wainright family.
worn out (page 11)
   see under *parts* above.

JOHN STEINBECK
unsimplified

FICTION
The Pearl
The Wayward Bus
Cannery Row
The Moon is Down
The Grapes of Wrath
The Long Valley
The Red Pony
Of Mice and Men
Saint Katy the Virgin
In Dubious Battle
Tortilla Flat
To a God Unknown
The Pastures of Heaven
Cup of Gold
East of Eden
Sweet Thursday
The Short Reign of Pippin IV
The Winter of Our Discontent

GENERAL
A Russian Journal
Bombs Away
Sea of Cortez *(in collaboration with Edward F. Ricketts)*
The Forgotten Village *(documentary)*
The Log from the Sea of Cortez
Once There Was A War
Travels with Charley
America and Americans

PLAYS
The Moon is Down
Of Mice and Men
Burning Bright

A SELECTION OF GUIDED READERS AVAILABLE AT

UPPER LEVEL

Of Mice and Men *by John Steinbeck*
Bleak House *by Charles Dickens*
The Great Ponds *by Elechi Amadi*
Rebecca *by Daphne du Maurier*
Our Mutual Friend *by Charles Dickens*
The Grapes of Wrath *by John Steinbeck*
The Return of the Native *by Thomas Hardy*
Weep Not, Child *by Ngũgĩ wa Thiong'o*
Precious Bane *by Mary Webb*
Mine Boy *by Peter Abrahams*

For further information on the full selection of Readers
at all five levels in the series, please refer to the
Heinemann Guided Readers catalogue.

Heinemann English Language Teaching
A division of Reed Educational and Professional Publishing Limited
Halley Court, Jordan Hill, Oxford OX2 8EJ

OXFORD   MADRID   FLORENCE   ATHENS   PRAGUE
SÃO PAULO   MEXICO CITY   CHICAGO   PORTSMOUTH (NH)
TOKYO   SINGAPORE   KUALA LUMPUR   MELBOURNE
AUCKLAND   JOHANNESBURG   IBADAN   GABORONE ·

ISBN 0 435 27263 2

© John Steinbeck 1939
First published in Great Britain by William Heinemann Ltd 1939
This retold version for Heinemann Guided Readers
© Margaret Tarner 1978, 1992
This version first published 1978
Reprinted seven times
This edition published 1992

Illustrated by Jenny Throne
Typography by Adrian Hodgkins
Cover by Caroline Binch and Threefold Design
Typeset in 10.5/12.5 pt Goudy
by Joshua Associates Ltd, Oxford
Printed and bound in Malta by Interprint Limited

96 97 10 9 8 7